CW00924624

The Empowered Woman

By
Kate Magic

First published in the UK by Raw Living Publications 2019
This is the second edition, published 2020
Copyright © Kate Magic 2019
Copy editor: Claudia Cahalane
Layout and design: Simon Earl
Cover photo: Tobias Pearson

No reproduction without permission. All rights reserved. No part of this publication may be reproduced, stored in, or introduced into a retrieval system, copied or transmitted by any form or by any means - electronically, photocopy, recording or otherwise without the permission of the copyright owners.
The right of Kate Magic to be asserted as author of this work has been asserted in accordance with Sections 77 of the Copyright, Designs and Patents act 1988.

Raw Living Publications
23 Ford Rd, Totnes, Devon, TQ9 5LE

Printed and bound in the UK by Acanthus Press.
ISBN: 978-1-9161381-0-0

Contents

For all the empowered sisters in my life who show me how strong I am when I feel weak, how beautiful I am when I feel drained, how adored I am when I feel unloved, and how happiness is always only a good, juicy conversation away.

For any woman who takes on the world on her own terms, and manages to do well outwardly, while still maintaining a strong healthy connection to her own inner magic.

For all the women who know that they deserve more, my wish is that this book reveals to you that more is not just possible, it is already yours; it's all there inside of you, waiting to be poured out and manifested into a welcoming and receptive universe.

To my hormones, for being so damn changeable, and so forcing me to look past the whims of my biology, deeper into my core, to find out who I really am.

We are in a time of great turbulence. I believe this is because we are moving out of the masculine age of the past few thousand years, into a more feminine one. But rather than framing it as any kind of battle of the sexes, and infer in any way that somehow men might lose out in this scenario, I prefer to use the terms objective and subjective.

The world I grew up in had us believe that there is one objective viewpoint that we all must adhere to. It tried to push us all into conforming to this one single narrative: a narrative that was defined by the white male heterosexual viewpoint. In insisting that we can all fit into this one narrow worldview, we were all reduced and diminished. The point we are in now is a mass awakening into a more subjective reality. An understanding that everyone has their own unique perspective on the world, and all these perspectives are equally valid. And to go beyond just accepting the validity of this multi-dimensional understanding of humanity, and to allow that when we give permission to each individual to explore their own uniqueness, we add to the richness of the human experience, and we all benefit immeasurably.

This time that we are in is about coming to terms with the fact that there is no one right way of doing things, no one way to see the world, that there are as many viewpoints as there are humans, and all these viewpoints are equally valid and equally relevant.

I hope in reading this book, you approach it with this very perspective. This book is simply my own personal thoughts and ideas, based on my own life experiences. I am not imagining that I am presenting a single overarching narrative that every single reader must be in total agreement with. I am a white heterosexual woman; I am aware of the huge amount of privilege that comes with, and I am not trying to speak for anyone other than myself.

What I do hope is that, although you may not relate to every chapter, there is at least one epiphany moment in here for you that changes the way you see yourself and the world. I hope that moment, or those moments, help you move your life in a direction that supports you in your own unique path.
I also feel the need to state that my feminism comes from a deep love for

men, as much as women. This book is in no way about giving them a hard time. It's the reverse. It's about asking that we women look at the ways we give away our power to men and the unhappiness and dissatisfaction this causes. It's a call to women to understand and take responsibility for our behaviours so that we can be gentler, kinder and more loving to the men around us.

"Feminism is a tremendously underestimated force, viewed in the present context primarily as a woman's concern. The understanding has not yet percolated throughout society that the advancement of women is a program vitally connected to the survival of human beings as a species. The reason for this is simply that institutions take on the character of the atoms which compose them, and what we are most menaced by in the twentieth century are dehumanized institutions. If women played a major role in policy formation and execution on the part of these institutions, I think they would have a far more benign and ecologically sensitive kind of character. So I see feminism not as a kind of war between the sexes or any of these stereotypic images, but as actually a kind of effort to shift the ratios of our emphasis that is expressed through our institutions" **Terence McKenna**

As I start putting digital pen to paper, I'm not sure exactly what this book is about, but isn't that typical of a woman? At times I may come across as neurotic, hysterical, or confused, but that's just how us women are, isn't it? We are over-emotional, and that makes us not as good as men. Not as good at thinking clearly, making money, achieving status, all the things that matter. Really, there are many other things I should be doing right now: cleaning up downstairs, seeing how the kids are, answering all the problems people need help with over email, working on my business. I don't even know why I am wasting my time on this book. Trying to work out what I really think about life. Trying to express how I really feel about the world. Why would that be important to anyone? I'm a woman and what I really feel is secondary to the need to make everyone else happy. And looking nice. Looking pretty is definitely more important than what's going on in my head. As if to prove the point, I painted my nails before I started work on this draft. My nails are pretty. My thoughts might not be, so much.

Introduction

"I feel that most of our belief systems and internal thoughts about who we are, what we are, where we are, what we should be, who we should be, relationship models, measures of success, race, class, religion, sexuality, and gender are not really our own but constructs created mostly by white men of European descent based on fear, oppression, power, and general ignorance on the diversity of the human experience."

"We are living with antiquated thought and behaviour. I hope this opens a few minds because when one suffers because of difference we all do.

Being able to self define and the ability to self authenticate oneself is very powerful and the only way to healing and self love." ***Honey Dijon***

When I turned 40, it seemed like a bit of a joke; I still felt far from grown-up. But around the age of 42, I started noticing big shifts in my personality. My priorities altered: the things that were important to me changed, and for the first time in my life, I started looking in the mirror and seeing someone who couldn't pass for a kid anymore.

To be honest, it was a shock at first, and it took me quite a lot of adjusting to. But I realised I had entered the stage popularly called "menopause," (technically, the perimenopause), and I became fascinated by hormones. I was the same person, living life the same way, but due to fluctuating hormonal levels, I began viewing my choices and lifestyle very differently. It became apparent to me that, although we like to think of ourselves as independent creatures, with free will and autonomy, we are, at times, little more than a set of walking biochemical impulses - and, all our decisions and life-choices are based upon what those biochemical impulses are telling us. They really are running the show.

The further down the rabbit hole I got, I realised hormones weren't just dictating my female cycles. They were also the main factor in causing feelings of stress and depression, the two great modern plagues that so many of my friends and clients (and myself, at times) struggle with. Understanding hormones also helped me understand more clearly what stress is, what depression is, and the steps we can take to avoid them. Or, to manage them, at least.

Even more pivotally, I understood that, due to the different hormones in men's and women's bodies, men and women - in general - can perceive reality in very opposite ways. Through comprehending these hormonal drives much more than I ever had before, I had many epiphanies. I had moments where long-standing mysteries were solved, and the nature of male-female relationships became much clearer than it had ever been before.

At this point, I realised this had to be a book. This was everything my girlfriends and I talked about, everything we struggled with in our lives: stress, depression, and relationships. The wake-up call of perimenopause for me was that for the first time in my life, eating well and having a positive outlook wasn't enough to keep me on top anymore. I had to pay real attention to this thing called hormonal balance if I wanted to stay happy and healthy. Understanding hormones is crucial to our understanding of ourselves, our bodies and our lives. With this knowledge tucked under our belts, combined with an adaptation of sound dietary principles and a spiritual mindset, we will likely have all we need to stay strong in this world. But without it, no matter how well we eat, how often we exercise, and how many gurus we study, we can still be seriously out of harmony with the world. As someone who had dedicated the last 30 years to studying health, diet and spirituality, this was something of an epiphany. For me, hormonal balance is the missing piece of the jigsaw, the crucial key to health that we all miss in our hectic 21st century lifestyles, and I imagined that if it was so revelatory to me, it would be to many other women as well.

I hope you find this book enlightening and exciting. I hope it proves to be a guidebook for navigating your own ups and downs in life. It's the book about being a woman I wish I could have read decades ago, it would have saved me a lot of trial and error. I would've made more informed decisions and had a much richer understanding of myself. The modern Western lifestyle isn't particularly kind to anyone, but it is definitely not kind to women. In understanding the ways society lets us down, we can stop blaming ourselves, and start creating changes in the way we live, what we tolerate, and how we shape our lives. In seeing how we might let ourselves down, we can learn to restate our value and set better boundaries – change always begins with that one individual step. Hopefully then, future generations, our daughters and granddaughters, will be able to look back on our current compromises and limitations with horror, thankful that the world isn't like that anymore.

What is Empowerment?

Empowerment is knowing that everything that happens in your life is ultimately a reflection of your inner state. And change happens through working on the inner and being at peace with the reflected outer. This is not a finite action with an end goal, this is a daily practice that deepens and becomes more profound over time.

Empowerment is knowing that you are living in alignment – your heart and your mind, your thoughts and your deeds, your body and your spirit, all operate and interact from the same intention, with the same purpose. The meanings we give our lives can be many, but alignment involves a meaning that springs from a deeper place of wisdom than that which occupies the surface of life. It comes from that unseen place, and it has its own logic: a logic we do not need to understand, but we come to understand that it is easier to obey and to trust this unknowable force, rather than to doubt and to question it.

Empowerment is knowing that there is nothing to be scared of and nothing to be worried about because every moment of life is a gift and a blessing. We expect, we welcome, and we treasure the blissful moments, because we know we have earned them, we deserve them. We do not flinch from the struggles and the traumas, because we know they are what make us strong, they are what give us our power, and when we welcome the lows as readily as we welcome the highs, we can recognise them as the wonderful gifts they are.

This is empowerment. Standing strong in oneself. Accepting of it all. Ready to embrace the full rainbow spectrum of our days.

A disempowered life hovers always in the grey areas, never tasting the fullness of life, constricted, frustrated, and blaming others for their situation. A disempowered life disconnects, and separates the different parts of itself as a survival mechanism to get through the day: I will be this person at work, and this person with my partner, and this person with my friends. Because to allow one of those aspects of my life to see the fullness of who I am would disintegrate the whole charade, and that's something I can't risk. A disempowered life is always scared of what's around the corner because their foundation is unstable, they know it doesn't take much to topple it. A disempowered life is dependent on others to perpetuate a sense of self, because a person is not drawing from source, and so a disempowered life is always insecure and vulnerable.

Knowledge of self is the most important gift we can give ourselves. Take time out from chasing around like a headless chicken, as the world would have us do. Dive into the waters of your consciousness, and know you cannot drown no matter how deep you go. Empowerment is freedom, true freedom, and freedom is a scarce and precious commodity these days. It's gold: the more you have of it, the richer you are, and it's a wealth far more rewarding and substantial than anything the material world can ever offer.

What Are Hormones?

Hormones

We are encouraged to think of ourselves as independent beings, making rational choices based on logic and common sense. The more I understand about being human, the less I feel my thinking mind is running the show. We are multi-faceted, highly complex beings, making decisions based almost entirely on irrational factors: past failures and successes, future dreams, but rarely, very rarely, based solely on the information that is in front of us in the moment.

If the ego is not the driver of its destiny (however much, for self-preservation, it likes to think it might be), what is? What is shaping our impulses and driving us on?

I got into food because I wanted to make my machine as efficient as possible. I wanted a high performance vehicle to navigate this lifetime in. Food seemed to me the primary fuel that this machine used, and I thought if I sorted that I would be in control of the machine.

It wasn't so. Food taught me about the mind-body connection, in that the food we eat has a profound effect on our consciousness. By making informed choices around food, we can create clarity, focus and intent in our lives. We can steer the ship much more effectively. But there was still a missing link. When we talk about mind-body connection, what do we actually mean? Something must connect the mind and the body, it's not just an abstract concept.

We are talking about hormones. Hormones were only first discovered in 1936. We drop them into conversation like we know exactly what we are talking about ("Don't worry about me, I'm just hormonal"), but actually what we know is most likely the tip of a massive iceberg.

Essentially, hormones are biochemical impulses. A signal is sent out, triggered either by an external event (eg being chased by a dog), or an internal event such as a women's monthly cycle, and that signal has an effect somewhere else in the body. These signals connect the brain and nervous system – they are literally the mind-body connection. A neurotransmitter, in case you are wondering, is almost the same – it's a chemical that transmits information from nerve to nerve within the brain. Both hormones and neurotransmitters are present in such tiny amounts in the body, and move around very quickly, which is why it's such a developing science: it's very hard to track and measure them and so begin to understand their purpose and effect.

This was one of my first major epiphanies. In holistic health, we are constantly referring to the mind-body connection - the concept that your thoughts influence your health, more than most of us are ready to admit. The state of your body has a direct impact on the state of your mind, and vice-versa. Here it was, laid out objectively to me for the first time. It wasn't just a New Age hunch: the mind-body connection is an actual thing, and that thing is hormones.

It's impossible to say which comes first, behaviour and brain chemistry are so inextricably intertwined. The more stressful or traumatic our childhood (and it's rare the person who passes into adulthood unscathed and intact), the bigger the effect that has on our brain chemistry, and we will behave differently to someone who had a relatively safe childhood. Cortisol is the main stress hormone (more of that later), and it's been shown that the more cortisol a women produces while she is pregnant, the more quickly and easily her baby will become stressed once it's out of the womb. Someone who has a stressful childhood is biochemically less able to deal with stress as an adult, which is setting them up with a disadvantage for life. Although, fear not(!) scientists used to believe our genes were immutable, but epigenetics is the emerging science of studying our ability to alter our genes with lifestyle and behavioural changes. Whatever patterns you are holding in your DNA, you have it within your power to change. One of my favourite sayings is that a habit is only a habit when you are unaware of it. Once you become conscious of it, it becomes a choice. Once you are aware of your patterns, it's always within your power to choose a different route forwards.

Yesterday, I saw a large sign that said: "We can't change the way the wind is blowing, but we can learn to adjust the sails." Whereas we can't change our external environment so readily, it's relatively straightforward to adopt techniques that help us change our thoughts and behaviour, in order to change the situations they are creating. When we begin to relearn behaviours in this way, that starts to create a new level of hormonal balance, which impacts all areas of our lives (more on these techniques in Chapter Ten).

The more I looked into it, the more I felt that hormones were the answer to everything. All our problems in life are primarily down to not understanding the power of these little biochemicals. Consequently, instead of being our allies, they turn into tyrants. Messing up our relationships, forcing us into misjudged career choices, cultivating stress and depression. If only we understood these biological impulses better, we would be kinder to our partners, and kinder to ourselves.

All the books I read seemed to over-complicate matters. Particularly the ones aimed at women – they all started with the assumption that hormones are problematic and worked backwards from there. But I prefer to assume instead that the body has a natural intelligence. I like to imagine that this vessel has been divinely engineered to work perfectly, immaculately even, when treated properly. ***If we recognise hormones as the powerful, life-sustaining force they are, instead of thinking we know better and working against our biological imperative, we might start making cleverer life-choices and end up happier than we ever dreamed of.***

So, having established that hormones are the connecting signals from the subconscious mind that create behaviours in response to the environment, the next pivotal fact to take on board is that **modern lifestyles are not conducive to hormonal balance**. If they were, I wouldn't be writing this book, and you wouldn't be reading it. Practically everything about our modern lifestyles is working against our hormones, and with disastrous effects.

Let's look at the main hormonal disruptors in modern lifestyles:

Pollution in the air and water – synthetic oestrogen enters the water supply and is very hard to remove. If you are drinking or bathing or cooking with tap water, then you are exposed to excess oestrogen, which is linked to declining fertility in men, and breast cancer in women, among other things. Traffic pollution has been shown to increase leptin levels, which is a main contributing factor to obesity.

Chemicals & pesticides in food – "hormone disruptors" such as the industrial chemical BPA found in plastic, mimic hormones and so disrupt natural hormonal balance. The most commonly used group of pesticides - organophosphates, lowers testosterone and disrupts thyroid balance.

Carbohydrate addiction – we are getting into a controversial issue nutritionally here, but to stick to the basics, if you rely on carbohydrates for fuel, you're also affecting your insulin levels. Even whole grains are going to cause fluctuating insulin levels and create stress in the body, which impacts all the other hormone levels. We need to look at why carbohydrates are so addictive: it's connected to serotonin and dopamine levels, which affect our mood and general happiness. It's a complex issue, which we will get into later..

Electromagnetic radiation – Also known as EMFs, have been shown to inhibit the release of melatonin, the most important sleep hormone. Insomnia is a common health issue nowadays, and that would be partly down to the proliferation of Wi-Fi and mobile phone signals that we are all bombarded with. Also, low melatonin has been associated with breast cancer.

Stressful busy lifestyles – the normalisation of stress is one of the biggest culprits in disrupting our hormones, I feel. We are encouraged to be addicted to stress in our culture, scared to quit the rat race. As women, we are taught that we can now "have it all" and try to cram several lives into one, taking on long working hours, a hectic social life, a busy exercise schedule, all while maintaining a beautiful home and the perfect family. The way we are constantly overdoing it causes elevated cortisol, and cortisol is really running the show - it affects all the other hormones. It also means we run off our adrenals, leading to adrenal fatigue and burnout. Ironically, the more we try to keep up the appearance of an impossibly utopian existence, the more we risk causing massive damage to our bodies and shortening our lives.

Sedentary lifestyles – exercise releases endorphins which then trigger the release of feel-good hormones. Someone who is sitting for over eight hours a day is going to have low serotonin levels. It's vital to move for as much of the day as possible.

Undealt with emotional trauma – as mentioned earlier, if we don't deal with the stresses that we pick up in early life, we carry them around with us, and respond accordingly. Time spent unpicking our unconscious programming and relearning behaviours is a wise investment for our health, but the message we are fed is "Keep Calm and Carry On" aka repress it all until it kills you.

How hormones affect us

We will get deeper into some of the specific hormones and their different functions shortly, but for now, let's look at their overall role in the body. From my research, I think the most important thing that we can understand, is that all the different hormones form a kind of web, as they interact with each other constantly. With our linear minds, we find it easier to understand concepts as a nice simple bullet point list, we want a reductive explanation that we can tie into a single package and file away in our minds. But hormones are messy and complex, and that's what makes them difficult for us to get our heads around. They simply do not work in a linear fashion: you can't understand one without understanding it in relation to the others. It's more helpful to think of a Rubik's Cube: as one facet gets completed, another gets altered. Every time a hormonal impulse occurs, it affects other key hormones to varying degrees. You cannot isolate them out from each other, they are completely interdependent. But to summarise as best we can, hormones control:

Weight gain & weight loss – the thyroid hormones, leptin, and insulin are the major players here.

Depression – is largely dependent on serotonin levels, dopamine also plays a big part in mental health.

The stress response – when this gets out of balance by constantly piling on the stress, it leads to chronic fatigue and all kinds of serious health issues related to the other factors on this list.

Women's cycles – adolescence, pregnancy, breastfeeding, menopause, as well as the monthly cycle, are all dictated by a bunch of hormones, including oestrogen and progesterone.

Sleep cycles - insomnia is usually hormone related, and down to a cortisol imbalance, and/or low melatonin.

Relationships – the success of your relationship with your partner revolves around how your hormones interact with each other, and for men and women that precarious oestrogen/testosterone balance.

We could break it down even further and just say, essentially, hormones play a part in just about everything that happens in your body. Chances are, if you are struggling with a health issue, we just mentioned it here. And while none of the above are life-threatening in themselves, if left unchecked, they will spiral out of control and lead to the more chronic and all too prevalent conditions such as cancer, diabetes, heart-disease, osteoporosis, and kidney failure. It's not that hormonal imbalances cause these chronic conditions, more that they set the stage for them to take root in the body. You can be out of balance and not develop a chronic condition, but you are unlikely to develop a chronic condition if you are already in hormonal balance.

OK, so this is life-changing stuff! Why didn't we know all this before? Hormones have a key role in our lives, yet we continuously neglect them, and with damaging consequences. Let's get on to exploring some of the main hormones and how they facilitate that mind-body connection.

Adrenaline and **cortisol** are the stress hormones. The adrenals sit above the kidneys, so in Traditional Chinese Medicine (TCM), strengthening the kidneys equates to strengthening the adrenals. The vast majority of us in the West live in a permanent state of adrenal stress, caused by insecurity in our homes, our careers, our relationships, or even all three. This insecurity causes us to work too hard, too long, not relax enough, not sleep enough, and has a knock-on damaging effect on all the other hormones. Anyone who drinks coffee every day is hammering their adrenals. I would say adrenal fatigue is one of the main health imbalances rampant in our culture today, so rampant it has actually become normalised, and not being stressed is actually the exception!

We'll go into this more thoroughly soon, but basically, the stress hormones are released when the body interprets a dangerous situation; they were designed to defend us against lions and tigers but nowadays it's more likely to be call centres and traffic jams that trigger them. Problem is, the body can't differentiate between a potentially life-threatening situation, and a mere temporary inconvenience – it's all the same to your stress hormones. They basically shut down all the other systems and rob all the energy to deal with what they see as an emergency, but in doing so, they mess with all your other hormones, and it's why constant stress can lead to thyroid disorders, digestive disorders, menstrual disorders, and problems sleeping.

Cortisol is highest around 8am and 4pm, and drops to its lowest between midnight and 4am. This is another reason why stress interferes with sleep cycles – if you have elevated cortisol, you might find yourself feeling wide-awake after midnight when you need to be resting. As we mentioned, oxytocin is blocked by cortisol, but so is testosterone – so stressed women become less caring, and men lose their drive. And if all that wasn't enough, cortisol and adrenaline release magnesium from the cells, and magnesium is the main mineral for the heart (if you want the technical jargon, it "stabilises electrical conduction in the cardiac muscle"). Hence stress depletes the heart energy.

Diet is really important in relation to cortisol – elevated cortisol causes insulin resistance, and is a major contributor to Type 2 Diabetes. To balance cortisol levels, it's important that we don't skip meals, and enjoy a low-glycemic diet. But we've got a whole chapter on stress coming up, so we'll leave it there for now.

Melatonin is the hormone that controls the sleep cycle. It is produced by the pineal gland, which is where the third eye is situated - our seat of creativity. Descartes called the pineal gland "the seat of the soul." Melatonin is happiest when the body gets to sleep and wake at the same time every day. Melatonin imbalance is also rife in our culture, which is why so many people are suffering from insomnia. Creative people tend to be night owls, because the pineal gland is more active at night – it activates around 9pm, which is when we naturally feel sleepy, and then melatonin levels are raised for around 12 hours. Production of melatonin is inhibited by light, so it's important to sleep in as dark a room as you can in order to stimulate melatonin production. Teenagers produce melatonin later in the day, a few hours later than adults, and then they need more sleep, again an extra couple of hours. This is partly what makes being a teenager so stressful, and teenagers so grumpy – if you can't fall asleep until 1 or 2am, then you're going to need to sleep until 10am or even 12 midday, yet we don't allow them that luxury. Sleep is one of the most powerful nutrients – we wouldn't deny our children food while they are growing, so why do we insist they are permanently sleep-deprived? On the other hand, as we age, we produce less melatonin and so need less sleep. Melatonin levels are one of the main factors associated with anti-aging, which is why sleep is important for a youthful appearance, and a bad night's sleep can add years to us.

Oestrogen, progesterone and oxytocin are the main female hormones. Oestrogen and progesterone, as we have mentioned, exist in a delicate balance, and when this balance is out of whack it causes all the common health issues women in the West face, such as PMS.

Oestrogen and progesterone work in a see-saw action – we'll get into this when we cover menopause. Oestrogen dominance is a common hormonal imbalance, but oestrogen levels can still be low, it just means progesterone levels are lower. This is why you can't just get a test for your hormone levels, it's all about the interplay, and this changes according to where you are in your cycle, and how much stress you're under. Oestrogen is one of the most interdependent hormones, hence women are more prone to mood swings – it affects dopamine, and boosts serotonin. PMS is largely down to this low oestrogen, low serotonin situation, which is why taking natural serotonin like cacao, mucuna and St John's Wort is effective. Oestrogen is produced in the ovaries – a healthy woman will actually produce small amounts of testosterone, which then converts to oestrogen. It rises from the time of menstruation until ovulation, and then declines mid-cycle from ovulation back to menstruation.

Progesterone is produced in the second half of our cycle, from days 14-28. It's made in the ovaries, and also in the pituitary gland and the adrenals *– when we enter perimenopause, production from the ovaries starts to decline, and the adrenals take over, which is why women approaching menopause don't handle stress so well, they haven't got the spare reserves* (there's a 75% drop in progesterone leading up to menopause!). Progesterone is the main pregnancy hormone – pregnant women's bodies are literally swimming in it, as it more or less doubles during this time. Progesterone also affects hair growth – so women that have had babies tend to be hairier than those that haven't! I can tell when my period is coming because suddenly my legs urgently need waxing. The upside (for those who are bothered by this kind of thing), is that after menopause, hair becomes less of an issue because of declining progesterone levels.

Oxytocin is the bonding hormone and neurotransmitter, produced during cuddles (with both humans and animals), sex, breastfeeding and during labour. Women release much more than men, so we have a greater need to bond, and are more sensitive emotionally - it's why girls and women are more likely to sleep with a teddy bear or end up as a crazy cat lady! It's released by the pituitary gland, but the main site for oxytocin receptors is the gut (which is why women tend to be more intuitive – their gut instinct is more developed). It's also interesting to note that women produce more oxytocin than men during love-making, so they are more likely to think they are in love after intimacy. Doesn't matter if their sexual partner is a personality match or not, our hormones overpower our rational minds, and crave more of that bonding and connection. Oxytocin is released by both men and women in the initial stages of being in love – it's sometimes known as the Trust Hormone, and it's what keeps men faithful (which generally goes against their testosterone-driven nature, as testosterone interferes with oxytocin). Oxytocin reduces cortisol, so when we feel in love we are less stressed, but equally too much stress in a woman's life diminishes her oxytocin levels and prevents her from being her natural caring, nurturing self. Lastly, progesterone inhibits oxytocin production, which is one of the many reasons the contraceptive pill isn't such a good idea, as it messes up the natural progesterone-oestrogen balance, and keeps women out of touch with their natural femininity. But don't worry if it all seems a lot of information to digest! We'll be going into this much deeper when we get into relationships in Chapter Four.

Testosterone is the main male hormone, although women produce testosterone as well. Testosterone is very directional, it's about focusing on a goal and achieving it, finding solutions. When our testosterone is depleted, we need "cave time," that is time alone, staring out at the horizon. Most commonly nowadays we find that by watching TV, going online, or more traditionally men would go out to go fishing or watch a football game. It's very important to men that they get this time without distractions, in order to feel fully functional in the world. Testosterone is associated with vitality and self-confidence – and men typically make ten times more of it than women!

Serotonin and dopamine are the main happy chemicals. On average, women produce 50% less serotonin than men, and also it takes us twice as long to restore serotonin levels, which is why women are so much more prone to depression (twice as much more, unsurprisingly). Serotonin levels are restored by talking! This is why women need to chat more, and feel talking solves problems, whereas for men, cave time is more important to them when faced with a problem.

Dopamine is about drive and desire. The more dopamine we produce, the more get up and go we have, the more motivated we feel in our lives to make things happen. Women more easily run out of serotonin, whereas men run out of dopamine. Dopamine deficiency is associated with both Parkinson's and Alzheimer's, whereas excess dopamine is contributory to schizophrenia, and the euphoria that comes from taking cocaine is basically a massive dopamine rush – so we can see how vital balanced dopamine levels are to cognitive health.

Serotonin is made from tryptophan, which is found in foods like turkey (hence its starring role in Christmas and Thanksgiving), pumpkin seeds, and cacao. It is converted to melatonin by the pineal gland, which is another reason why depressed people might have problems sleeping. Stress depletes serotonin, which is why stress and depression are so interlinked. Most importantly, 95% of serotonin receptors are actually in the gut, which explains why eating well has such a positive effect on mood. We will dive further into the world of serotonin in the chapter on depression.

The **Thyroid** hormones, T3 and T4, control metabolism. People with an overactive thyroid (hyperthyroidism) find it hard to lose weight, and people with an underactive thyroid (hypothyroidism) find it difficult to put on weight. Both of these problems can be linked to iodine deficiency.

Leptin is the main hormone that regulates the appetite. Diabetics usually have leptin resistance, which causes them to always be hungry even though they have an elevated blood sugar. The more fat cells you have in your body, the more leptin is produced, and the lower your appetite. So if you have low leptin, your body stores more fat, in order to produce more leptin. And if you have elevated leptin, you become leptin resistant, which means you also store more fat, and never feel satiated!

What we've just covered is a very over-simplified picture so we can begin to get our heads around what is a very complex operating system. Hopefully, you are beginning to understand it's not as much about amounts, as that the hormones are all naturally interweaving harmoniously, and that balance really comes from lifestyle choices that we make, the thoughts we have about ourselves and our belief systems about the world.

Rather than thinking of hormones as old-fashioned couriers, riding out on their bikes with a single parcel to a definite destination, *it helps to imagine them rather as their own world wide web, feeding messages back and forth between each other*, constantly adapting and changing in response to the information they receive, never static, always unfolding.

Hormone Characters

Let's have a party. Let's have a party and invite all our best friends. They are dressed up in their finery, and they want to have a good time with us. They want to get to know us better, and for us to know them better. They are all friends, old friends going way back, and they've spent so much time together that at times their characters can become indistinguishable. They have all influenced each other, helped shape each other, and they all work together to keep you healthy and happy.

Meet your hormones

Serotonin is a happy little bugger. Always got a big smile on his face. He has a sunny disposition, and when he's around, you relax, everything seems like it's going to be ok.

Dopamine is friendly, but a little pushy. He has a lot of drive, he's the one that makes things happen. Serotonin might sit around happily watching the grass grow, but dopamine wants to put that positive energy to productive use. He's always onto the next thing, always seeking what's just out of reach. He's super enthusiastic.

Adrenaline is so fun to be around! Adrenaline makes everything exciting, euphoric sometimes. But it's such a rush to be around him, he tires everyone out. After just a short burst of his company, you're feeling exhausted and in need of retreat. You have to learn to politely ask him to leave, or he will just hang around wearing you down, and you might get upset with him.

Cortisol hangs out in the background more, he's not out there like some of the others. But he's running the show more than you think. All the others depend on cortisol, and if he runs low in energy, everyone's in trouble. Whatever you do, don't overlook him like he's not important, because then he'll make you sit up and take notice. Treat him well!

Oestrogen is the mother of the group. Always checking to see if everyone's ok. She can be a bit of a worrier, and sometimes she gets the others down, especially serotonin and cortisol, but she only wants the best for everyone at the end of the day.

Testosterone now we are talking pushy! Testosterone wants to be the best in the group. He wants to do everything first and make sure everyone knows. The thing about him is though, he is very strong, and that makes him kind of useful to have around. He loves doing things for other people, sorting out problems, he's the fixer to oestrogen's worrier.

Oxytocin we all love oxytocin. She just wants to cuddle and snuggle. Like oestrogen and testosterone, she wants to do things for you, but she just gets happy off caring for others, there's no agenda with her.

Progesterone she's a bit of a bitch, actually. She speaks the truth that not everyone wants to hear. She can be cranky and harsh, but only because she's usually given a bit of a rough deal. Most people aren't comfortable with the truth. If they were, they would recognise her for the wise old crone that she is.

Patriarchy

So much of what we do is predicated on the internalisation that men are more important than women. Look at social media, and the overwhelming message from women is one of seeking approval; the overwhelming message from men is one of stating their dominance. By overturning that idea within yourself, by accepting yourself and loving yourself, and knowing your value, you are changing the fabric of our culture. ***You will probably lose friends over it, because a woman who is not seeking approval nor allowing herself to be dominated is a threat to the status quo. But you will gain the heartfelt gratitude of the woman of the future for clearing the way.***

Structural Sexism

Our Western world is ruled by Caucasian males. This is not rhetoric, this is fact: our heads of state, politicians, judges, bankers, media moguls and so on, are overwhelmingly white, male and heterosexual. Our fundamental structures are created by heterosexual white men, and so automatically support the way a heterosexual white man's mind works. Thus if you are a woman, or of non European descent, or of a different sexual persuasion, it takes more effort to operate in the world, than it does for a white man; it is harder to get by. They have set the rules, and they have set the rules with a clear and definite bias to suite themselves. People who are the other sex or of a different race find all kinds of invisible barriers set up that hinder their progress. We are so accustomed to the world in this fashion, that rather than recognising the inherent bias in society towards a certain way of thinking, a certain way of being, we more often blame ourselves for being deficient in some way. We see ourselves as inferior. Rather than trying to influence the world in a different way, and create new structures that are more balanced and equal, we try and mould ourselves to fit the existing structures, which usually makes us feel uncomfortable and even depressed.

This is what structural sexism means: that the attitudes that favour one sex over the other are so embedded in the structures of our society, we are brainwashed into them from such an early age, that we take them for granted, we cannot even perceive them. I believe that there are as many men as women who would appreciate a society where the balance was more equal. But as the dice is loaded in the man's favour, it takes them longer to perceive the injustices. It's harder for them to see how society is set up to support certain groups and not others, because they are less likely to directly suffer from this discrimination. And a small minority of white men have come to believe that they actually are superior, and dominate the cultural agenda, hence the racist, sexist and gender-normative attitudes that still prevail, and seep through into every area of our lives.

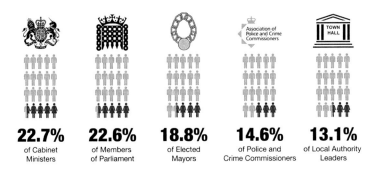

Who Runs Britain?

countingwomenin.org

The Pornification of Our Culture

An obvious example is the pornification of our culture, where women are constantly reduced to sex objects. Defenders argue there is nothing wrong with seeing a beautiful body on display, and feminists should lighten up. But how would it be if these were images of virile black male bodies everywhere? Black men are often stereotyped around sexual prowess and being generously endowed. How would those men who say there is nothing wrong with a female body on display feel, if these flagrant images were instead of black men with bulging biceps and tight shorts? Next time you are walking in a public area, imagine every semi-naked woman you see in the shop windows and advertising hoardings as a sexually posed black man and see how differently it makes you feel. Look at the people around you and imagine their responses. Men would probably feel offended, insecure, threatened. Women might start to see black men in a different light, to see every stranger from a new, often uncomfortable, sexualised perspective.

Now we can see where the idea "she was asking for it" comes from. It's nothing at all to do with what signals the woman is sending out, but down to the fact that men are used to narrowing women down to a simple object of arousal. Perpetual exposure to images of women in prone positions, semi-clad, teaches them subconsciously that women are always available on a sexual level. When they see a revealingly dressed woman in real life, they might then conflate her with all the female performers they've seen on billboards, adverts, and music videos, who were "asking for it". A sexy woman can be a thing of breath-taking wonder and beauty, but when we over-saturate ourselves with these images, it's greedy, and what should be a special delight saved for intimate occasions becomes more like junk food, something that's mass manufactured without heart and soul that leaves a nasty taste in the mouth.

Can you identify with that as a woman? Do pornographic images of women make you uneasy? Do they make you feel sub-standard? Are they encouraging the idea that that is the most valuable way a woman can express herself, by gift-wrapping herself as another object of consumption?

I am confident in my body, and I am no stranger to short skirts and low cut tops. But I like to choose when I feel like expressing myself in this way, and I don't want to be made to feel that I have lesser worth if I choose not to put myself on display. I also hate that if I do choose to show my legs or my chest, I feel that in certain places and situations, it can be dangerous to look a man in the eye in case he takes it "the wrong way." He will conflate me with the millions of objectified women he has seen in his life, and assume that I am making myself available, rather than recognising that I am expressing my individuality. I also feel disturbed when I see a group of women coming towards me all dressed like prostitutes, and acting as if this demeanour actually does grant them superior status. How would men feel if it was fashionable for them to wear revealing clothes? If when you went out in the evening all the other men were sporting tight shorts and bare chests? How disturbing would it be to your sense of manliness to see every other guy in the place dressed up like Tom Jones? It would make you feel uncomfortable, alienated, and spoil your night out. But as a woman it's virtually impossible to go out on a weekend evening and not encounter a group of women like this. I have to bite my lip, steel myself, and wonder whether I should be laughing or crying.

But sexuality is the mere tip of the iceberg. The objectification of women is just a cover-up for a whole plethora of other ways in which women are diminished or downright ignored. As a single parent I felt this injustice daily. Before I was a parent, I barely noticed it, actually I think if you had asked me did women have equal opportunities I might have answered yes. Once I became a breastfeeding mum, I was no longer sexually available, and it was only then I became aware that the freedom and opportunity that had been afforded to me previously was largely based on me being young, single and not unattractive. ***Once I was pushing a buggy, not only did those opportunities recede sharply into the background, but I began to experience what it felt like to be a substandard citizen*** – someone who didn't fit that profile of the elite and therefore had to make excuses and justifications for themselves in the world. And once I became a single parent, I felt the full force of the inequality hit home.

When I was a child, stay at home mothers were not unusual. In fact if I am remembering rightly, I think they were the majority. Women who made no excuses for revolving their own life around their families; women who got the kids ready for school, did the housework and the shopping, were there for the kids and their husbands when they came home. These women managed to fulfill their role as a mother and a wife, hopefully without undue stress: in the evenings they had time to put their feet up, watch a bit of telly, and still be in bed before midnight. But now that has become impossible. It's very rare that I meet meet a stay-at-home mum these days and if you do, she is likely to be apologising for herself. A woman is expected to also have a life outside of the home, and while it is wonderful to have options and increased economic freedom, and something I do not remotely take for granted, what this inevitably results in is stress for someone who is trying to fulfil too many roles without enough societal support. Currently, there is not the framework built into our institutions for a woman to both easily manage a career and still be present at the heart of her family. Some families do make it work, if the man can afford to take a step back in his career, if other family members can step into the breach, or if there is a big cushion of wealth available to spend on domestic help. But for too many women, this pressure to take on an equal share of the financial responsibility and keep focus on building a successful career, means that her womanhood suffers as a result.

"Chasing payments and negotiating fees cause me stress regularly. They cause survival anxiety, and make me aware of the glass ceilings that exist." **Ysanne**

In the UK, women only won the vote in 1918 – and even then you had to be over 30, married, and a property owner to vote! Less than 100 years ago, that's incredible. And if you study the newspapers of the time, the political and media response to this wonderful moment of progress was shocking, they made these women out to be crazy. They put about a thousand suffragettes in prison, and when the women went on hunger strike, they force fed them. It puts it all into perspective. These are our great-grandparents, no wonder there is still such an undercurrent of sexism in our culture.

While being grateful for our freedoms, it's important to recognise how young and immature these freedoms actually are, and how far we have to go before the feminine principle has the same influence over our lives that the masculine principle does.

The Patriarchal Disease

It's common for women to feel like the veil is being lifted from their eyes when they hit perimenopause. Before menopause, our over-riding biological urge is to make babies, and to do this our primal instincts tell us to be nice to men, and behave in ways that are accepted by the tribe. Once this biological imperative is dropped, we stop being such people-pleasers, and start seeing the world in a different, and some would argue, more realistic light. I have always been aware of the ways women are reduced to objects and their voices repressed, particularly as an adolescent and when I became pregnant. But as I entered perimenopause, these increasing jolts of awareness really became like a hammer repeatedly hitting me on the head. Patriarchy is a disease that most don't seem to realise they have. In all areas of life, we are allowing men to dominate, sometimes unabashedly, but often in such subtle ways that it's barely perceptible.

Men are traditionally used to defining women, deciding who a woman is in relation to him, and have the woman conform to that. A woman who knows herself, is connected to her feminine, is in her power, will resist that. This bewilders, confuses and often annoys men. The easiest way for him to deal with it is to simply ignore her. There are plenty of women who will play the game, why does he need her? Therefore, powerful women are most often ignored, which is incredibly damaging for our culture, and our female role models become those who are less positive, less empowering. A lot of the time, if a man cannot manipulate a woman, he does not know where to place her within his framework of reality, so he rejects her.

There are three ways a woman can be accepted by the patriarchy: women who use their sexuality as their currency are valued because they are easily objectifiable, and therefore controlled; women who have internalised the idea that they have a lesser self-worth and are therefore happy to occupy subservient roles are accepted. Women who can prove their self-worth in terms that men can understand eg, competitiveness and control, are accepted, albeit grudgingly. But a woman who has gained her self-esteem through dominion of self, through expressing the fullness of her femininity, is too much of a challenge to the male status quo, and she must be shunned and cut down.

Everyone likes to be surrounded by people who think like them, this is human nature. Men like to surround themselves with other men, that's natural. They give each other the positions of power. They support each other's voices. In the majority of cases, I would venture that it's not so much that they are intentionally shutting women out, but that they unthinkingly give their male voices predominance. They have unconsciously internalised the idea that that is how they think and what they say is more important than the fairer sex. In every single situation you enter, look and see who holds the authority, and who is in servitude. It drives me crazy! I love men, but I get tired of hearing their viewpoint always. Everything is off-balance. The whole conversation is off-key, because the male viewpoint dominates the entire culture, inside and out. To be heard, women must be twice as talented as their male peers, and be prepared to knock on doors twice as hard. If they are in a lucky position where their uncompromised voice is heard, and they are allowed to express themselves freely, they should expect twice as much criticism and be prepared to be continuously reduced, devalued and side-lined by their male peers.

Bjork, one of the greatest female role models for my generation, spoke out in a Pitchfork interview in 2015, when she said, "I want to support young girls who are in their 20s now and tell them: You're not just imagining things. It's tough. Everything that a guy says once, you have to say five times. Girls are now also faced with different problems. I've been guilty of one thing: After being the only girl in bands for 10 years, I learned—the hard way—that if I was going to get my ideas through, I was going to have to pretend that they—men—had the ideas. I became really good at this and I didn't even notice it myself. I don't really have an ego. I'm not that bothered. I just want the whole thing to be good. And I'm not saying one bad thing about the guys who were with me in the bands, because they're all amazing and creative, and they're doing incredible things now. But I come from a generation where that was the only way to get things done. So I have to play stupid and just do everything with five times the amount of energy, and then it will come through." If a bold, innovative, outspoken genius like Bjork has to play these games, what hope is there for the rest of us?

Men are naturally more predisposed to being adept at logic, power, control, restraint, creating order. Women's strengths are empathy, community building, nurturing, creating beauty. (Please note that I am making mass generalisations here in order to create a broad framework of understanding, and believe that we all inhabit different places in the spectrum between the two end poles of extreme masculine and extreme feminine). Because the world we live in is run according to a set of rules created by wealthy Caucasian males, their values are seen as more important, more worthy than those of people with other backgrounds, different outlooks. This punishes us women, and makes it harder for us to be materially successful in the world, as the jobs that earn the most money are the jobs men are naturally better at. It also makes it harder for us to find inner peace and happiness, as we are less valued in the culture, so women are more likely to suffer from stress and depression.

"Being governed by psychopaths causes me stress. The most stressful thing in my life is the endless paperwork we all have to do just to be able to live a hassle free life. Not being able to pay my bills on time stresses me right out!" **Natalie**

Most of us are unaware of how we internalise patriarchy. In short, it makes women insecure and troubled. It is so hard to carve out a place in a male-dominated environment, that women who succeed tend to become hostile to other women, and guarded over what they have achieved, thus denying their caring feminine nature. In our boys' club culture, there's little access granted to women. A woman who has made it into the inner sanctum of the boys' club is less likely to want her sisters in there, because male attention to go around is so limited, she needs to be ruthless in order to keep as much as it for herself as she can. In other words, unless you are that rare being who has the self-awareness to preserve your femininity, and ridiculous amounts of determination, to be successful you have to be at least a bit of a bitch.

Clearly, these are over-simplifications for the sake of making a point, and not every single man is fiercely bent on upholding the patriarchy while the women around them ubiquitously flounder. But these are scenarios I see played out over and over again, in all areas of my life. I experience it first hand, and if you think hard about it, and keep your eyes open to it, you will realize that you do

28

too. Women get a raw deal; we internalise that, accept our roles as less worthy, less important, less necessary, less valid, less meaningful, and in doing so, we perpetuate our own diminishment. And we act out our insecurities in ways that are hurtful towards, and diminishing of, our sisters, rather than supporting them and holding them up.

"I watched my father emotionally abuse my Mum, and my brothers do the same to me, until I stopped the dance. It's all he knew and all my brothers know. They cannot relate to me as an equal and so I have no contact with them." **Roisin**

If we want to create a better world, if we want more peace, if we want less suffering, it's vital that we add our voices to the conversation. That we stop agreeing that we are second best, stop just agreeing with the way that men say things are, and know that our viewpoint can be radically different from the consensus, and that's so much more than simply valid – it's really important, and it needs to be heard.

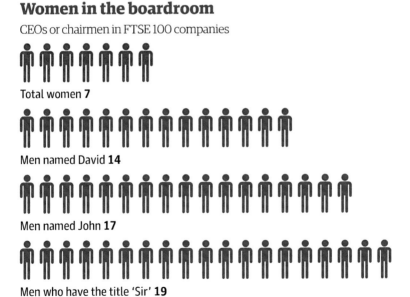

Women in the boardroom

CEOs or chairmen in FTSE 100 companies

Total women **7**

Men named David **14**

Men named John **17**

Men who have the title 'Sir' **19**

GUARDIAN GRAPHIC

Patriarchal Aggression

When oppression is so commonplace, it can be hard to identify, especially when it's unconscious. Jay Smooth is a US radio host and commentator who made an iconic video, "How to Tell Someone They Sound Racist." You should watch it if you've never seen it. He makes a point about people who say: "I'm not a racist but..." and then go on to make a racist statement. He says they might not see themselves as racist, but in that moment they are being racist. So racism isn't so much a state of being, as an awareness and a practice that we must be continuously engaged with in order to avoid falling into the default of the existing unbalanced paradigm.

I believe exactly the same thing happens with sexism. Theoretically, a man might believe that men and women deserve equal rights. And he might not believe that he is behaving in a patronising way and talking down to women. But the idea that men are superior because they are physically stronger is so deeply embedded in the male psyche. A lot of the time, he may not realise he is playing this role out with the women in his life. And ironically, the more attractive the woman is to him, the more she will be on the receiving end of this behaviour. That's because the man has a greater desire to prove his worth to her. It's hard to see it, but every time you feel patronised and belittled, remind yourself of this and take it as a compliment! And then do whatever is within your power to stop it being perpetuated. Remove yourself from positions that lay you open to this kind of behaviour. Bring up how uncomfortable it makes you feel, or how inappropriate it is as soon as it starts to happen, before it becomes a repeated pattern, worn into a groove. Don't attenuate yourself to keep the peace.

Our instinct, once a man raises his voice, tenses his muscles, or says something demeaning - is to turn the other cheek as a method of protection. But if you can see it before this instinct kicks in, or even as this instinct kicks in, then you can step back from your impulse, and give the man permission to do the same. If you reframe your response into one of holding your own and standing up as an equal, it gives him the opportunity to reframe his behaviour; he can retract the aggression, and proceed in a more peaceable and fair manner. On the other hand, it may make him more aggressive, as he is not used to being challenged in this way. But at least you are seeing the situation clearly for what it is and not allowing yourself to perpetuate the inequality. If enough women stand up to him in this way, eventually the man who is used to using his aggression as a tactic to bully his way through life, will get the message.

Think of a man that you find it hard to talk to, and it's probable that it's because he won't listen to your point of view. Many have a way of replying to a woman's questioning with an aggressive undertone that suggests that the conversation is closed, and if she wants to go into the subject further, he will become more aggressive. A woman instinctively know that in this battle of aggression, she is likely to lose. So she has to become very creative and emotionally intelligent in order to circumnavigate the way he has blocked her route. This can get very exhausting! Especially if it's in a close relationship with a romantic partner or family member. The constant vigilance for watching out when your freedom to express yourself has been curtailed, and then finding creative ways to get your message out somehow can take a lot of time and emotional energy. Maybe you have to learn to pick your moments; maybe you have to learn how to word things in specific ways that enable you to still get your point across. They are all ways in which a woman in her daily life has to try much harder in order to achieve a state of flow. A woman has to pick her battles and when there are so many to be fought, both major and minor, she may have to let a lot of these little remarks and incidents go.

"I hate it when we fall out and it makes me emotional, when I'm all tearful I can't think the argument through, and it frustrates him that I'm girly and crying!"

Another downside of this is that so many women are sensitive to being patronised that they then also bring that into their relations with women in power. It's very hard to be a woman in authority, because the perception is that women always need to be nice, and if they aren't all sugar and spice, then they are being bitches and/or divas. It's much harder for a women to assert authority without being challenged on a personal level. A woman who is unhappy and dominated in her life, will see the dominant woman as easy prey. She may not be able to speak her mind to the men who dominate her, but the female authority figure isn't an aggressor, so the lower ranking woman feels more able to express herself in this situation. It doesn't help a dominant woman that her male colleagues in authority are less likely to support or back her up. Their instinctive reaction is also to diminish a woman who is too high ranking. An alpha male is welcomed and appreciated by women, although he may be challenged by men; an alpha female is seen as a threat, both by the men and women. Hence again, the tendency is for the woman to attenuate herself to keep everyone happy. It's a very creative and emotionally intelligent woman who can be an authority figure without losing the love and respect of the people around her. They will want to typecast her as a harridan, and she may find it easier to just slot herself into that role rather than fight the stereotype.

Reproduced with kind permission of Maddie Dai

Recently, someone asked me if I could do something for her. This job would've taken about six hours to do properly. I regularly do things for this person without getting paid, so I guess she thought, why not add to the list? But when I received the email, it hit me in a very sore spot. The amount of requests I get to do stuff for free far outnumbers the people offering me paid work. I thought I'd do a pie chart.

Interestingly, it came out at 175 hrs a week – there's 168 hrs in a week, so I've worked in an extra hour a day, but you'll have to allow me that in a superhero kind of way.

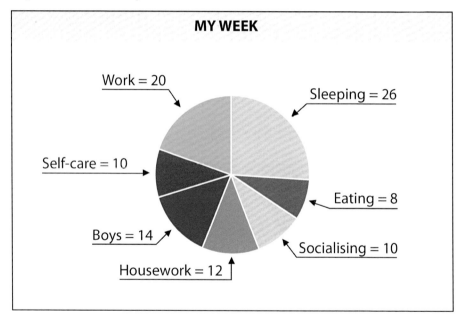

As a single-mum, the vast majority of my time is spent doing unpaid tasks - 26% on boys and the home. I have 20% of the hours of the week left for actually earning that little thing we call money.

In terms of the work that comes into my inbox – aside from running my business, and working on creative projects, there is a constant stream of people wanting interviews, articles, wanting me to mention their product or event, give them advice on some issue or another, wanting me to speak at their event etc. A small minority of these offers for speaking are paid, but even then, the fees they offer are usually pretty low.

So maybe you can see why I struggle when someone puts another request for unpaid work before me. Does she not realise I have a permanent to-do list as long as my arm? Does she not realise that I am often overwhelmed with the demands the boys place on me, without adults adding to my demands as well? I actually think this woman should have known better than to casually toss such a big demand my way. She is a parent as well. Why did she not?

Because it's so embedded in our culture, this denigration of women's work. This unquestioned assumption that housework and childcare is work that must be done without recognition or financial reward. And then, as women, we take that with us into the workplace. We ourselves have been accustomed to not valuing our work, our talents, our expertise. We shop and cook and clean for free, why not do all our work for little or nothing? This willingness to work for nothing: because we care, for the joy of service, in the desire to get the job done properly; this willingness spills into an arena where we should really be making a stand for real financial reward.

I think a large part of my struggle in coming to terms with the unmanageable workload of single parenthood involved a sense of betrayal and disappointment. It's a disillusionment which Naomi Wolf discusses so wonderfully in her book "Misconceptions." I was brought up to believe women had equal rights. "Women's Lib" had happened in the 70s and now we were free. How could I have been so lied to, so deceived? While I acknowledge that I have greater freedoms than my mother and grandmother, and while I appreciate the huge victories won by previous generations, particularly the suffragettes, what we now have is not equality and is certainly not freedom.

I watch as my male peers climb higher in their careers, as they do not have these extra responsibilities continuously begging of their time and energy. I watch people defer to the men in my field as experts much more readily than they defer to me – men who have the same or less experience are continuously imbued with more credibility, and because their work has a masculine approach, it is deemed superior. I frequently experience the way people find it easier to take instruction from a man, the way my business partner can so often get a better result than I can out of a situation, because people listen to an assertive man, where they more often feel challenged by an assertive woman.

I am getting clearer at learning to say no to things that serve other people but don't serve me. At first, I found it almost hopelessly difficult, because I'm hard-wired to please other people, like my mother and my grandmother before me: to overlook my own wants and needs and make everyone else happy regardless of what I might be experiencing. But I learnt (the hard way, of course), that if I don't put myself at the centre of my own happiness, no-one else is going to. ***We need to start valuing ourselves as women, and valuing each other. Not valuing ourselves in male terms, as in how attractive we can make ourselves, and how much we can do things for others, but valuing our very being, how strong and wise and authentic can we be? How can we stand up for what is right, how can we act within our core values, and so shift other people's values towards the feminine?*** We must no longer assume that our work is worthless. We must give each other credit at every opportunity. We must pay each other for our work, and if a financial interaction is a struggle, offer some other compensation: a meal, some babysitting, a massage. All three of those things would be so valuable to me, and indeed at many points in the decade I was a single parent, an offer of help in kind like that might have reduced me to tears of relief and gratitude.

I made it work because that's what I do. But it was so demoralising to be constantly asked to work for free. When the boys are asking for new clothes, and food, and money for a music lesson all in the same breath, while I have mountains of housework to surmount before I can even begin to start my "real work", it often felt like a miracle that I pulled it off. I am grateful for it because it has made me strong. I am grateful because it has taught me to believe in my powers of manifestation, and my ability to work magic. But I can't help wishing more people would recognise the value that women bring to the world, and the personal sacrifices so many of us make to achieve what we do. I meet so many incredible women when I teach my raw food classes: women who have gone through struggles and hardships but have managed to stay strong and positive. These kind of women do not get enough attention. Why do we find it harder to defer to the cancer-surviving mother of three than the businessman in the suit? Why do we put the young woman who dresses to please men on a pedestal so much more readily than the older woman who has wisdom and stories to share which are far more heart-warming and uplifting?

When my children were small it used to terrify me that I would get to the end of the day, totally burned out and exhausted from tending to everyone's needs apart from mine, and yet I had not completed a single money-making activity all day. I feel that most of the activities I am valued for, I am not paid for. Raising my kids, keeping an ordered home, nurturing my relationships, all these are things I put a lot of time and energy into. But modern society offers no rewards for these activities at all. You could be an exemplary mother, a wonderful home-maker, an incredible friend, but without someone else to financially support you, you will remain on the bottom of the social pile. ***There is so much pressure now on women to go out and compete in the world, and less and less value put on these traditionally female activities which are in reality just as vital to our personal health and the health of our society.***

"Being a single mother, working part-time and home educating my kids is amazing, but the financial stress and lack of time to stay on top of admin is stressful." **Inga**

This means that as women, we need to constantly restate our value, and make that clear to the world. We need to appreciate the enormous amounts of energy we put into making sure our loved ones' lives run smoothly, and ensure those around us truly appreciate it as well. We need to fight for a world where mothering is put at the centre of daily life, not pushed to the margins.

#MeToo

2017's #metoo movement marked a welcome shift in the way we view male and female sexual relations. But I think sexual harassment and assault is a symptom of a deeper issue, and that is the way men assume dominance in general. With their body language, with their speech, there is an innate assumption of superiority, which is reinforced by the patriarchy. Meaning the rules, the rhythms, the flow, the priorities of our day are set out to suit male narratives and push those forward. They reduce the feminine principles, and women's inclination within these systems is to diminish themselves and become subservient to those who appear to be stronger.

There are many ways we can begin to shift this but as always I believe when we start with the micro-actions, the bigger picture then naturally takes care of itself.

Body Language. Watch how you hold yourself, what signals you give off. Women are you subjugating yourself, making yourself smaller in order to keep the peace? Men, are you invading a woman's space and using your physicality to assert dominance? When I am in a public space I noticed constantly how men have a tendency to dominate that space. They will take up more room. They will energetically push into a woman's space and make her fold into herself. They will stand close and act like she is not there.

Verbal Language. This is displayed in the tone that is taken when speaking to a woman over a man, and lack of ability to hear clearly what a woman is saying without talking over her, dismissing what a woman has to say, laughing it off, assuming she will have an inferior viewpoint. A woman's viewpoint is likely to be different and that difference is valid and important, but instead it is more likely to be regarded as irrelevant.

"Men are taught to be more loud and vocal; some may call it arrogance, I see it as the pressure of non-failure applied to boys makes them blag their way through things that girls wouldn't do, as they are taught to ask for help, and I think that this skill helps men to make mistakes and take risks." **Rosemary**

39

Value Systems When a man asserts that his financial contribution is more valuable than the emotional contribution a woman brings, we are all diminished. When a man asserts that going out into the world and having a job is more important than the caretaking roles of cooking, cleaning, and caring everyone loses out. A lot of the unhappiness in our society comes from deciding that some jobs are more important than others and therefore should be paid more. Disproportionately, it's work that men regularly find easier to do that is paid more and work that women more often might find easier to do that is paid less, if at all.

I also think that men don't understand how they chip away at the very core of our power and security when they conduct these acts of micro-aggression. They don't see how they question our very right to exist in the form that is usually most natural to us. They don't see how deeply threatening that is to our sense of self and well-being. To them it seems minor, but to us it feels huge. I believe if they understood how major it felt to be on the receiving end of it, they wouldn't do it so readily. It's that lack of comprehension that is the heart of the problem, and that's why the most valuable work we can do is learn how to express ourselves authentically and openly, and without fear of compromise.

These almost imperceptible incidents occur so regularly that we may not even be aware they are happening. Incidents such as a man dominating us in a physical space; not hearing out what we have to say, or hearing it and disregarding the different perspective as inferior; or assuming financial superiority by rewarding some tasks disproportionately to other tasks. These kind of smaller details, which may seem insignificant in themselves, create a bigger picture which leads to the occurrence of the more significant transgressive acts, and uninvited displays of assumed superiority. These behaviours would not, could not, happen if all these threads of the story were not running in the background, weaving themselves into a culture where this huge imbalance is normalized.

Summary

- Structural sexism means that the constructs that place women below men are embedded into the very foundation of our culture.
- Women act out this fundamental insecurity and men act out an unconscious dominance in so much of what we do and say, without even realising.
- We need to learn to recognise the value of female traits eg nurturing, caring, connecting, sharing, holding space, supporting, as equal to the values of male traits.
- We need to take personal responsibility for demanding equal payment for our time, and stop over-giving and undervaluing ourselves.
- We need to stop seeking approval from others and give it to ourselves.
- We need to stop being competitive towards other women and instead create sisterhoods that make us stronger.
- We need to know our value as women isn't in how much we can do for people, it's in who we can be for them.
- Know that your voice is as important as anyone else's. In fact, if you're a woman, it's even more important that your voice is heard, in order to rectify the balance.
- Expect to have to work at least twice as hard and be at least twice as good as your male peers to get the same recognition.
- Expect to lose friends when people realise they can't play the old games with you, but expect that your new-found strength means you won't care too much.

Stress Hormones

Let's start with the bad news. The more research I do, the more it seems to me that it's next to impossible for women not to live with some level of stress in our current circumstances. Modern lifestyles practically guarantee burnout, given all the responsibilities we have to juggle, and the lack of support we receive from the wider culture. The good news is that we do have the power to change that, and it's vital that we do, not just for our health, but also for our daughters, and all subsequent generations.

The two main stress hormones are adrenaline and cortisol. These are the big baddies in our story. Most of us are running on these stress hormones, and in doing so, knocking all the other hormones out of balance. The adrenal glands are placed just above the kidneys – in Traditional Chinese Medicine, kidney energy is equated with adrenal reserves, and kidney formulas are designed to thereby strengthen the adrenals. The adrenal glands produce adrenaline and cortisol, as well as some other less notable hormones, and also the male sex hormone testosterone. You may well know adrenaline as the "fight or flight" hormone: it's role is to provide us with a surge of energy when faced with an enemy, so we can run or fight, but either way, survive. Nowadays, we are using it for all kinds of non-emergency situations – running for a bus, or fighting for a seat on the train – but the problem is, the body can't tell the difference between just another typical stressful day, or a life or death situation, and so faithfully keeps on spurting out the adrenaline regardless.

Cortisol acts slightly differently. Whereas adrenaline is more the result of a direct response to a particular event, cortisol has its own rhythm, peaking at 8am (when we should be most awake), and diminishing to a low about 4am. In a lot of people, the stress response is severely damaged, due to ongoing stress, so cortisol doesn't have a chance to normalise. This can lead to either elevated cortisol levels, or diminished cortisol levels, but the outcome is basically the same – adrenal fatigue. Again, the body is unable to differentiate between stress happening because a bear is about to eat you, or the stress happening when your boss is in a bad mood with you. Either way, it keeps chucking out the cortisol. When someone has messed up cortisol levels, it's going to impact on every other hormonal system. Production of all the other hormones goes into shut down, while energy is diverted to this emergency response. Insulin is affected, so it's one of the prime causes of diabetes and obesity; the thyroid hormone are affected, contributing to both hypo- and hyperthyroidism; it plays havoc with the gut and so is behind IBS and colitis; it's going to affect oestrogen and testosterone so impacts on fertility and sex drive.

Stress is addictive, so we get used to living off it and forget how it feels to be calm and relaxed. Moreover, in our current culture, stress has been normalised to such a degree that if a person is calm, relaxed and content with their lives, it has come to seem like they are in the wrong somehow. To be stressed and have problems and worries is the norm, it's what we all do. When we are caught up in these stressful cycles, it's hard to see what they are doing to us until it's too late. And it's hard to let go of stress; it becomes our raison d'etre. It's another way of hiding from ourselves, just like drug or sugar addictions, a stress addiction keeps a person from being fully present with themselves. We all know people who find things to get stressed about, even when there seems to be nothing, who love to blow things out of proportion and make a mountain from a molehill. When adrenaline is coursing through our veins, we feel alive and vibrant. When we are adrenally fatigued we feel like a shadow of ourselves, washed out, with little enthusiasm for life. So finding some reason to get ourselves worked up again brings everything back into focus, and keeps us from looking at the underlying dissatisfactions that are creating the low level stress.

The adrenal glands produce adrenaline, and they are situated just above the kidneys. If you want to do any kind of adrenal restoration work, a kidney cleanse is a great idea to get started (see Chapter Ten: Lifestyle Tips).

At around the age of 43, a women's oestrogen starts to decline. We are born with millions of eggs, but this number drops gradually throughout our lives, and then we experience a sharp drop off between the ages of 40-45. A woman still ovulates monthly, but there is less and less chance of her conceiving a baby. Menopause is said to happen when the monthly cycles cease completely (that's where the word comes from – it's a pause in menses). As the ovaries stop producing oestrogen, the adrenal glands take over. It's vital at this stage, that the adrenals are strong and high in reserves.

In this day and age, how many women hit their 40s feeling strong and high in reserves? Ha! That is actually a joke. Most women have been juggling career, children, partner, friends, the home, and putting their own wellbeing at the bottom of the list.

"The most stressful things for me are emotional fights, and having to deal with too many things in a short time. The best strategy against stress is to plan as much as I can, and not take anything too seriously." **La**

Actually, bang on hitting 42, I felt this enormous wave of depression wash over me. What was wrong with me? I remember sitting on a paradise beach in Goa, there to teach a sold-out course, surrounded by people who appreciated and valued me, yet I felt washed out, unhappy, dissatisfied. I was finally achieving the kind of lifestyle I had worked so hard for, why didn't I feel the joy and peace I expected?

I was exhausted, was the short answer. I had gone through a 10 year period of breastfeeding and pregnancy, beginning when I conceived Reuben in November 1996, and finishing when I stopped breastfeeding Zachary in May 2006, on his third birthday. I am truly, hand on heart, not exaggerating when I say I don't think I got an unbroken night's sleep in that whole ten year period. As well as breastfeeding, attachment parenting, home educating three energetic lively raw vegan boys, I had moved home four times, written two books, set up a business, and gone through a divorce all in the same period.

Now I look back, it seems crazy to me that I didn't see what I was doing to myself. But I was a product of my environment, a world that taught me you could never work too hard, and that you needed to struggle to achieve success. I had big dreams and I was determined to see them come true. I really had no idea about the cost to myself of pushing myself too hard. I thought I could just keep hustling and hustling, nose to the grindstone, and eventually I would emerge in the sunshine and be free to bask in its rays.

Well, emerge in the sunshine I did, but I wasn't so much in the mood for basking. I felt like I could sleep for a hundred years, that Velvet Underground song always going round in my head. I wanted to curl up into a ball and let it all wash over me. I thought there was something wrong with me. Me, Miss Positivity herself, always the one to look on the sunny side. Always the first to trot out, "Everything happens for a reason," and: "It will all be OK in the end." Had I been wrong?

I was adrenally fatigued, and it took a sinus infection that steadily started to worsen, for me to really take a step back and consider whether I was on the right track. Luckily, I knew all the right tools to take good care of myself. I was so grateful that I had got to a position where I could afford to slow down a little and not worry about how to pay the rent and feed the kids. But when I say slow down a little, I mean cut down to a 40-hour-working-week rather than a 70-hour one. And when I say 'not worry about finances', I mean I was just about able to scrape by instead of never quite scraping by.

What kind of world are we living in where that seems normal? That's the question we really need to ask ourselves. ***What prison have we created for ourselves where we have to live the lives of at least three if not five people, all rolled into one, all while being Instagram selfie ready? It's time, as women, that we are more open about the impossible pressures we face,*** and stop pretending that we can cope with it all, because really we can't. And, if you think you can - then sorry to break it to you, but you are probably heading for a nervous breakdown, or osteoporosis, or cancer, or worse.

It is impossible to be a woman if we accept all these rules and conditions. We joke about being superheroes, but we know we are just human and all too often, at the heart of that joke is a weeping clown.

"Taking on too much work for others makes me stressed, and I possibly take it out on my loved ones." **Lucy**

The answer, I believe, is to understand ourselves better, to recognise our limits, and to get better at setting boundaries. To not take on everyone else's everything so incessantly, but to become more of who we want to be. By respecting adrenaline and cortisol, ***by respecting our body's messengers, then maybe we really can become superheroes.*** If we can create a life for ourselves where we are operating from a strong power base, then the world will flow around that and we will be queens once more. You have to secure your domain, and then own it, and then everyone will listen. It's a battle many of us have to wage inch by inch, taking back our power one day at a time, forging out territories that our mothers and grandmothers never occupied.

What Is Stress?

"The function, the very serious function of racism, is distraction. It keeps you from doing your work. It keeps you explaining, over and over again, your reason for being. Somebody says you have no language, so you spend twenty years proving that you do. Somebody says your head isn't shaped properly, so you have scientists working on the fact that it is. Someone says you have no art, so you dredge that up. Somebody says you have no kingdoms, so you dredge that up. None of that is necessary. There will always be one more thing." **Toni Morrison**

Although this quote is about racism, I think it applies equally well to sexism, and when I first read it, it resonated with me deeply as I'd been considering adrenal stress a lot. For a long time, the subjectivity of stress had fascinated me. It's a much bandied-about word these days. We all talk about how stressed we are, almost as if it's a badge of honour, and I've written already about how confusing stress with success is a very dangerous and unhealthy pattern our society indulges. But what actually is stress? How would you define it?

Stress is very different for different people. Some people thrive on pressure, others avoid it. A stressful situation for one person is bliss for another. For instance, if you asked me to spend a day going shopping, watching TV and visiting my parents, that might sound like heaven to many people, but for me it would cause huge amounts of stress.

Stress then, is discomfort. It's feeling out of alignment with your external environment. It's feeling that something needs to happen before you can be comfortable again, and that that something is somehow out of reach. It's feeling like you don't have the means and resources to reach that state of comfort again, and it's accompanied by a deeply primitive sense that somehow your life is in peril. It sounds faintly ridiculous to say that going to a shopping centre would make me feel that my life was in peril. But all kinds of things are happening in my brain and my body that set off a series of hormonal reactions, which push me to a point of feeling out of control. After a very short while in a shopping centre, I start getting an overwhelming urge to flee, as if there were some kind of predator bearing down on me.

"I get stressed when I resist the flow of life and not trust the natural unfolding of nature's intelligence -thinking I know best!" **Roisin**

The main stress hormones are adrenaline, cortisol and norepinephrine, and it's these that are the measurable response to the variable response set off in our minds. They are age-old response strategies from the body that cannot determine the difference between a tiger or a traffic warden. To experience stress in our day to day lives is normal and healthy, but to experience prolonged stress is deeply damaging.

Sadly, virtually all of us, to varying degrees, are locked into stressful cycles. Repeated patterns of behaviour, which are discomforting to us, which we are unable to see a way out of from in our present position. As women and as carers, these stressors can be innumerable! Our dream is to wake up in a perfect house with a perfect partner and perfect children. And work at our dream job where we are creatively fulfilled, and recognised, rewarded and validated for our work. Ha! That dream is a far cry from the reality of modern living. There is simply not enough time in the day to maintain all the roles that are expected of us. Something has to give, and it may mean that you go through a long period of your life single so you can focus on your career, or perhaps you put your career on hold while the kids are small. Maybe you've chosen not to have children, or maybe you've decided to live with a messy and chaotic home. Whatever choices we make, it takes a very strong character to stand proudly by them and not take on society's judgments that we are inferior, and at fault somehow for being single, or childless, or messy, or poor.

The other option is that somehow you do juggle all the balls, that by society's expectation you have it all, the home, the family, the career, but we can all see where this is leading. Externally you might be ticking the boxes and looking good, but internally? The fourth wall of your life is you, and if that's not solid, the house is going to crumble - letting down not just you but all those other walls that are dependent on you.

The pressure is intense! Thoughts are continuously flitting through your mind unheeded, but they are all taking you away from your feminine essence and contributing to that build up of stress. The endless housework, the infinite attention children need, the monstrous effort needed to build a career in our male chauvinistic world, all the things you need to attend to for yourself, not to mention your friends. Your nails, your hair, your yoga class, buying new tights and tampons, the laundry, the washing up, the grocery shopping - these are just a few of the things that run through a women's brain taking up precious space. And let's not even go there right now with partners!

Next, what happens in this pretty much unavoidable stress trap that our modern lives have placed us in, is we start blaming ourselves. It's our fault that we can't do it all because we are too lazy, or not clever enough, or we slept in, or were "naughty" with what we ate or drunk. We are grumpy, we lose our glow, and then we start to build a negative perception of ourselves as someone unlikeable and unattractive. On a deeper level, we start going into all the stuff we inherited from our parents, but again, we'll save that for a later chapter.

This is where the quote at the beginning of the passage comes in. It's the patriarchal structures of society that force us into these positions, and it is emphatically not our fault unless we allow it be. We are trying our best but in a world where women's work is systematically undervalued and underpaid, we do not have enough support and recognition for everything that we attempt to take on, even if we are superwomen! What ends up being sacrificed most often is not the work that fulfills us, or the family we adore, the home that would fall apart without us, or the relationships we depend upon, but ourselves. *As women, we instinctively put ourselves last on that list and think our own inner health and happiness has the least value in the equation, rather than it being the cornerstone on which everything else rests.* We are so busy trying to prove ourselves, we overlook the basic requisites of what makes us happy and in striving too hard, we miss out on the simple pleasures of life.

I believe that it's this basic fault in perception that rests as a central cause for the vast majority of women's health ailments. From PMS to menopause, from breast cancer to heart disease, ***it's our attitudes to ourselves which determine our hormonal stress levels and our hormonal stress levels which determine our health.***

Consider long and hard what you take on. Consider how much of this is determined by belief systems inherited from your parents that you can re-evaluate. Watch how you respond to stress when it rears its head. Try to examine where the discomfort arises from mentally that creates the stress response in your body, and how for the good of all, you can eliminate that discomfort from your life. The deeper issues at stake will take years, if not decades to find solutions for, but that shouldn't put you off, it will be well worth it in the long run. And you may find that there are many smaller connected issues that can be more easily and quickly resolved by just changing your thinking around them.

The key is - rather than seeing stress as a weakness and something we need to make excuses for, we need to recognise the injustice of the structures that create those stresses, and to believe in our own abilities to strengthen ourselves in order to create lives that are not diminished in this way. ***Most importantly, we need to learn to honour ourselves better, have clearer boundaries, and ensure we have a fountain of energy to draw on to competently carry out our demanding and multi-faceted roles as women in the 21st century.***

From a health standpoint, it's essential that we do this work if we want to live long and vital lives. Managing to survive at breakpoint may be all the fashion right now, but guaranteed at some point, probably in your 40s or 50s, those brakes will wear thin and you'll come skidding off the road in a dangerous crash.

Progress may be slow at times, and patience may often wear thin, but this isn't just a personal battle, it's a redrawing of the gender roles that future generations of women will benefit from, and as such it's some of the most important work we can be doing.

Let's take my previously mentioned shopping trip as an example. In a shopping centre I feel overwhelmed on many levels: the noise, the brightness, the electro-magnetics; it's too much stimulation. My immediate conscious reaction is to be disturbed and perplexed by the number of people who seem so intent on purchase. Any situation where I can't find the humanity troubles me in this way: when there's so many people grouped together, such as in a packed commuter train carriage or in a shopping centre, but everyone puts up walls, no-one makes eye contact or smiles, it confuses me, and I have difficulty dealing with it. That gulf between what is real to me as a belief system and what is real in my apparent experience is hard to straddle. So to combine this mental conflict with the added physical disharmony of the space, means I am pushed into such a place of discomfort that my logical mind becomes overwhelmed and starts to shut down, and my primal instincts take over.

I have suffered from panic attacks throughout my adult life, and a similar pattern always occurs. Fortunately, they don't occur often, and now I know what they are, I am better at dealing with them, although they did used to freak me out a lot in the early days. Women are twice as likely to suffer from panic attacks as men. In a panic attack, the primal part of my brain takes over. Rationally, I know my problems are not life-threatening. But my body starts to react as if they are – I start to hyperventilate, and if it develops, I start to scream. All I need, actually, is someone to calm me down and comfort me and tell me everything is OK, and I can come out of it pretty quickly. But if people around me react negatively – with distance, scorn, worry, confusion, even panic, then that makes it worse, because the signals I am receiving externally are confirming to my brain that something is wrong. This is an extreme example, but I think it's easy to see how an accumulation of external signals, combined with an accumulation of subconscious symbols, cause the brain to create a story which is based on a more primitive experience of being human than the one which we are currently living.

So now think of a situation in your life which you personally find stressful, where you feel that fight or flight response that prevents rational thinking, and try and identify what aspects are physically challenging, and which are a conflict created in your mind. In my shopping centre example, the physical aspects are really quite minor, but it's the stories created in my mind that set the stress reaction into play. So how can I examine these stories and try and reconstruct them to avoid the stress release? And secondly, how can I find ways to create a life for myself where I don't have to put myself in those kind of discomfiting situations? We will go into this a lot more in Chapter Ten, but what's important for now is to affirm to yourself that stress is a subjective experience rather than a life-threatening experience. And, there are ways that you can remove it from your life, rather than accepting that it will continue to threaten the very core of your wellbeing.

A major part of dealing with stress, is finding ways to let go of it. So many of us are addicted to stress, addicted to the drama, because we are afraid of what's underneath. So we keep recreating patterns in our lives that are taking us away from who we truly are, who we truly want to be. It's vital that we step back, wherever possible, and take a long hard look at what we are creating and examine whether it's what we really want. When you have negative belief systems about yourself, whatever you do in life is going to perpetuate that belief system. For example, if you hold an inner unaddressed belief that you don't deserve money, or it's hard to make money, you could be wildly successful but still manage to lose all your money somehow. If you have a deep-rooted belief that men always cheat on you then yes, even the man of your dreams will cheat on you (or you will accuse him of cheating on you and walk out on him anyway, as one of my friends did).

When you are centred and grounded in your love for yourself and your life, then you allow space for the universe to work its magic. The universe wants to shower you with love, appreciation and abundance! That's just how it works, and only you are blocking that with your out-dated belief systems. Upgrade them now. We are in a new era where everything is so much more possible than it ever was. Show up everyday, and dream your biggest dreams, have faith, and watch how things shift for you.

Media Stress

Open up any women's magazine, no matter the target age or background, and you will find an endless parade of lifestyle advice. On the one hand, this can be seen as a healthy desire for self-improvement, but more often the media exploits women's insecurities for its own gain. Instead of endless lists of how to lose weight, how to be less tired, how to be a better wife, we should be asking why women feel the need to ask those questions in the first place! Why are women concerned about their weight, and feel uncomfortable in their bodies? Why do women feel tired and need energy pick-me-ups? Why do we feel that our relationships aren't satisfactory as they are? It's not that men couldn't be asking these questions of themselves either. But for some reason, they are not trying to fix themselves! They do not seem to come, generally, from this same place of insecurity. And to me, the answer is obvious, it's because if you're a white heterosexual male, you occupy the dominant place in society and so you make sure that everything is tweaked to suit you. For those who don't like it, rather than taking on board the others' experience, and allowing it to be valid, it's easier to belittle and mock them, make sure they know their place, and continue on, as blithely as before, making the other feel their experience is less valid.

Next time you feel that you need to make some personal changes, sure, go ahead and explore different perspectives on your happiness, but equally don't forget to question your discomfort and from where it arises. If you don't examine the underlying structures that are contributing to your lack of inner peace, all the self-help books in the world aren't going to get you where you want to go. If your current discomfort is coming from the sense that you can move forward into a more aligned and harmonious place in your life, then it's worth putting in the work. But so often, the change that we desire needs to come from the world. In which case, it's important to dig your heels in, step back, and move into your goddess power. Don't make yourself not enough; don't make yourself tired, stressed, exhausted, overworked, undervalued, or any of those roles that we slip into so readily when we are trying to change the world. The world doesn't need more burnt out women! The world needs more goddesses, full of love and positive energy, who are working on their healing for the good of one and all. Come back to your inner square one, and then move forward and create change from a place of peace and harmony. ***Ignore a media who would have you focus on your perceived failings and insecurities. Instead, learn to love yourself, and then you can challenge the ways in which the world isn't loving you back.***

So many times, I see my peers take on more drama, when they are already unhappy. They've already got too much going on and not enough time for themselves. But they imagine that another responsibility, be it a work project, a child, caring for a sick friend, will be the thing that proves them to the world and makes the world love and accept them. It doesn't even have to be big things; often it's small things, like embarking on a long and arduous journey to do something that isn't that important or fun, or worrying over something that really doesn't matter much to anyone. Every time we act this way, the signal we send out into the universe is not that we deserve more love, but that we deserve more stress! And so many women chase endlessly down this path until they end up with a chronic illness that hopefully then offers an opportunity to pause and reassess their direction. Please don't take this route. Please, if you are already on it, turn back now. Try instead showering yourself with love, real true self-love, and watch the universe shower you with love in return.

A big pattern I have observed is around the way men use money as a way to control women's behaviour. Of course this doesn't happen in all male-female relationships, but I believe it's a worryingly common scenario. A man will undervalue his partner in some way. He will say or do something that diminishes her, makes her feel disempowered, inadequate, not good enough. It may be a small thing and to the man it might feel inconsequential. But actually, what they are doing is bringing the whole weight of the patriarchy down upon the woman. Her reaction might seem extreme, over-emotional. But what she is receiving is not just a criticism about her appearance or that she forgot to buy some shopping or something that the children did; she receives the whole oppression of a system that is constantly telling her that however much she does, however hard she tries, she is not good enough. *And in this system, that power is measured by money.* The man is more likely to hold the financial advantage because caring for your appearance and doing the household shopping and being a therapist for your loved ones are all tasks that we are not paid for. So the man's withdrawal of approval also brings up deep survival issues, as well as all our vulnerabilities and personal inadequacies, and our anger against a system which is weighted so heavily against us. We want our partner to be someone who we can be vulnerable with; that's the very heart of the intimacy bond I believe, that the man feels he is providing security, and the woman feels that she is safe to lean into that space. So to feel that he is withdrawing that space can be huge and scary.

What seems to happen in these scenarios, is that the man is a little cruel, a little harsh. The woman becomes emotional, upset. The man then gets even more angry at her display of emotions, and the situation becomes her fault, because she is making 'too big a deal' out of something. Then he shuts down, and won't communicate more, leaving the woman stewing in her perceived failures and vulnerabilities. Reconciliation occurs once the woman has picked herself up off the floor and moved on, but it rarely comes from the man accepting the part he played in starting it or in making any effort to understand why the woman is so upset. The woman internalises all this as her weakness, her problem; she might share it with close family and friends, but she accepts it as the way things are. It is rarely aired in public spaces and examined as a deep dysfunction in our society, which damages us all.

What we need to address is how to shift the blame in this pattern, away from women being the ones at fault because they are unable to keep up with the demands of the patriarchy. Alongside the double burden of needing to suppress their true feelings in order to attempt to satisfy these demands. Instead we might start to examine how men both withhold power from women by expecting them to fulfill an unequal amount of unpaid roles, and by disallowing them a voice to express how damaging this is to them on a fundamental level. When we can find ways to correct this imbalance, our whole society will flourish and become so much healthier, with men benefitting just as much as women.

I feel this is one of the most crucial ways that otherwise strong, independent women are held back, and one of the first and most obvious things that needs to be done for women to take an equal place in society. ***We must find ways for women to not be pushed into positions of extreme vulnerability while they are doing caring work.*** The most clear example of this is as a parent, but there are many other instances where women take on the burden of unpaid labour in caring for a relative or partner, or just the household. She then finds herself in a position where she needs to hold back from her true expression of self, and live with her power on hold, rather than risk the security of those she is caring for.

"This masculine money energy and the huge sadness that it brings for women. How we mothers turn ourselves inside out to make it all work out until we are burnt out from giving... I wonder when men will see and appreciate that we are not money making machines but care-taking powerful loving mothers." **Erica**

56

Summary

- Stress is pretty much inevitable for women in the West, so you need to have strategies for dealing with it.
- You cannot be everything society needs you to be, so pick your roles and don't sweat the rest. Set limits.
- The two main stress hormones are adrenaline and cortisol, pay attention to them.
- Stress is a measurable response set off by a variable response: identify your personal variants in order to modulate your inevitable hormonal response.
- If it's external factors that cause you stress, examine how you can avoid those situations, and relearn more appropriate boundaries for yourself.
- If it's inner behaviours that create stress, watch to see how you change those thought patterns. Pay attention to your stories and see how you can rewrite your own narrative.
- Develop faith. Trust in the moment. Allow what is and work with it. Don't disconnect from, block or deny what's really going on for you, but embrace it and use it to take you to where you want to go.
- Don't allow anyone to exploit your insecurities, so that you go and create more stress in your life. Learn to love yourself and then start from that power base to create more love in your life, rather than imagining love is something that must be earned.

Depression

"I am grateful for every layer of this cake of life I'm here to take an ecstatic bite out of, even in light of not knowing the flavor of each bite. All I need to know is, I created it, so the recipe was custom-made enrichment that I knew I could stomach. The deeper I choose from my heart, the sweeter each layer." **Tania Marie**

So now we've got a clearer understanding of our internal landscape, through learning about hormones, and a clearer understanding of our external landscape, through examining the patriarchal structures, it's no surprise to add these two things together, and come up with our next topic, depression.

Depression is something of a taboo, it's seen as a failing, but I prefer to see it as a healthy response to an unhealthy situation. I believe our natural state is bliss, and depression arises from the way the wellbeing of the individual is undervalued in our societies, and the lack of channels for pure unadulterated joy that our society provides. In the same way that cancer is the body's healthy defence mechanism gone awry due to the amount of toxicity it has to deal with, so is depression the mind's attempt to signal a lack of balance, and seek to reconnect with its natural ecstatic state in a less than ecstatic environment.

Serotonin is the main happy chemical in the brain. We naturally create it when we are happy. The drug Ecstasy, or MDMA, creates a huge serotonin spike in the brain, which is how people become ecstatic on it! But unfortunately, it then creates a massive serotonin deficiency when it wears off, which is how it becomes addictive, and also messes with brain chemistry when taken on a long-term basis. Most prescription anti-depressants are SSRIs, which divert the natural uptake of serotonin in the brain, and artificially introduce it. Again, this creates dependency, and also has a damaging long-term effect on brain chemistry. But both these examples help us to understand how crucial serotonin is to our state of well-being. **Women use up serotonin twice as fast as men! And it then takes us**

twice as long to rebuild serotonin levels. These two factors are crucial in understanding ourselves, and explain why women are twice as likely to suffer with depression than men. Couple this biochemical disadvantage with the fact that our lifestyles aren't set up to support women's needs, and it's almost inevitable that women will suffer from at least mild depression at some point in their lives.

Do you know one of the quickest and easiest ways to rebuild serotonin? Talking! This is why women need to talk about their feelings much more than men. We actually need to talk to feel ok, whereas men don't have the same biochemical need, *they are more content in their caves.* Another way is eating chocolate. Chocolate contains precursors to serotonin, so when we eat it, it encourages the brain to create more. It actually strengthens the neural pathways, rather than damage them like prescription or recreational drugs. If you are really concerned about your serotonin levels, you can also buy 5Htp, which despite its chemical sounding name, is actually the natural precursor to serotonin, or take the Ayurvedic herb Mucuna (also known as Kapikkachu), which is also high in 5htp, or the traditional European herb St John's Wort (more about these in Chapter Ten). These three supplements all assist the body in producing more serotonin, and help us to restore natural alignment.

Dopamine is the other main happy chemical. Dopamine, you may remember, gives us that get up and go that we look for. Think about when you have an exciting new project to undertake and you can't wait to get started with it – that's the feeling of dopamine in the brain. Dopamine is all about seeking out activities to light up the reward centres in the brain – the warm glow that we get when we have the satisfaction of fulfilment and completion in a task. Men's work is likely to trigger more dopamine release, as it tends to be targeted towards set goals more eg, fixing something broken, building something. The work women often take responsibility for tends to be less goal-orientated and more concerned with general maintenance eg, laundry, cleaning, raising children. Women are much less likely to receive that dopamine hit in their work, because it's much harder to see the end result of their tasks. Instead, the woman is more likely to feel depressed because no matter how hard she works, the job is never done. And there is very often no-one to appreciate this work – no-one to congratulate her on how hard she has worked that day, no-one to praise the amount of time and effort she put in to the task. More likely, someone there to complain that they've run out of cereal, clean socks or she hasn't spent enough time with them! So again, the dopamine centres are not being triggered. A man who works hard is much more likely to receive adulation and financial freedom for his work; a woman is more likely to end up with simply just more work! When a woman is seen as capable of getting a lot done, people will gravitate to her as someone who will get things done for them, happy to increase her workload without extra reward – one of my favourite sayings is, *"If you want something done quickly, and you want it done well, ask a busy woman."*

To increase dopamine levels, you need to set yourself goals, and give yourself rewards. Don't rely on others to do this for you! Be on the lookout for activities that are within your budget and time capabilities that you can incorporate into your routine to get your dopamine fix for the day. On days when I am working from home all day, running the business, doing the housework and being with the kids, I need to have something to look forward to at the end of the day, or my drive starts to diminish. If I have something really fun I am anticipating, I can get twice as much done in the day because my motivation is much higher. And I always have an external goal that I am working towards, something that encourages me to get my necessary work done so I can enjoy my own fun project. For me, most often that turns out to be writing another book, but it could be the development of any artistic skill, working on your home, travel – whatever keeps your dopamine levels up and engaged. However far-fetched, **having a goal of your own, beyond your immediate responsibilities to others, is essential for your fulfilment.**

Biochemically, as well as serotonin and dopamine, you also need to look at your:

Oestrogen/progesterone – these two need to be in balance, and low oestrogen means low serotonin. This is an essential part of the Rubik's cube for women. Birth control pills mess with this delicate balance. As does dairy. And stress. Women are three times more likely to suffer from depression during perimenopause because of declining oestrogen levels. I found St John's Wort invaluable during perimenopause for boosting my diving serotonin.

Cortisol – yay our favourite hormone! You've got to love cortisol – of course he plays a part; he plays a part in everything. Low serotonin and high cortisol is the textbook picture for depression. If you're stressed you're going to be borrowing from all the other systems to keep that cortisol burning, remember? So when you have elevated cortisol, everything seems harder because all your resources are depleted. It's like you're in permanent fire-fighting mode. You have to take things down a notch, and step backwards before you can step forward again in the right direction. We went into cortisol in depth in the previous chapter about stress, but in our modern lifestyles, stress and depression are almost inextricably intertwined. That feeling of overwhelm, lack of fulfilment, of always having too much to do and not enough time; working too hard and not getting enough time for yourself: that's the classic picture for women trying to juggle family and career, and it's become normalised to a dangerous degree.

Thyroid – one of the main symptoms of hypothyroidism is depression. Hypothyroidism is one of the most misdiagnosed illnesses today. If you are exhausted, depressed, and can't lose weight, consider upping your iodine levels and getting a blood test to check your thyroid hormones. One in 50 women in the UK suffer from weak thyroid.

Why Women Are Twice as Likely to Suffer with Depression

We can see that we women have the dice stacked against us in a variety of ways, most of which we've covered already, but it's worth listing them again for clarity.

- PMS messes with our hormonal balance every month. Whereas men can pretty much know how they are going to feel from one day to the next, women are more likely to vary from wildly social to massively introvert in the space of a few weeks. Our needs fluctuate to a much greater degree, so it's much harder to forecast how we might be able to meet them, and therefore it's much more likely they won't end up getting met (more in Chapter Six).

- Raising children is an intense and exhausting period which isn't given the high status it deserves in our culture. Women can be working harder than they've ever done in their lives, but for less financial reward, and less attention from a culture that values appearances so heavily. It's a time when we are very unlikely to be getting our needs met because we are so busy meeting the needs of our children, and it seems that society is not keen on supporting us in getting anywhere (we cover this in more detail in Chapter Seven).

- Menopause is a time that throws up a lot of undealt with stuff for virtually all women. It's a time when our energy reserves drop suddenly, when actually we need a lot more energy to deal with the change that is upon us and sustain our responsibilities. It can be very difficult to juggle getting to the heart of what this change looks like and how we might meet a new altered set of needs, with the weight and pressure of whatever life situations we have built up around us. For many women, finding a place for their new self can feel hopeless in their existing landscape (this is the subject of Chapter Eight).

- Women are more likely to be in an oppressive situation, dominated by others by family members or work colleagues. This can manifest as direct abuse, but it doesn't have to be so extreme; any way in which a woman feels she is restricted in her authenticity and unable to enjoy freedom of expression is likely to cause depression.

- Women are more likely to internalise, and blame themselves for their problems. Men are more likely to externalise! So in a relationship between the two, a common scenario is that the man can be emotionally draining, and expecting a lot from his partner, which will clearly make the relationship dysfunctional. But when it becomes overtly dysfunctional, both parties blame the woman. Women have a tendency to take on board far more than they need to, and then think it is a failing because they can't cope.

- Women often see it as their responsibility to make everyone around them happy, and when they can't do that, it makes them feel inadequate.

- Women are more likely to be judged on their appearance than for their personality or intelligence. This puts undue pressure on women, especially young women, to look and behave a certain way, and to feel that they are not good enough somehow if they can't meet the impossible standards that magazines and TV shows set.

"I get depressed when I am purposefully disempowered and undervalued. If someone is acting badly towards me, on purpose, and they can get away with it due to our relative positions in society, that's depressing."
Ysanne

Getting Your Hormonal Needs Met

Understanding the hormonal differences between men and women is really key in understanding our world and our lives. Men's and women's needs work in opposition and the problem for us is that modern lives are designed to support men's biochemical needs but not women's. We are encouraged to go home at the end of a day of work, and watch TV or go online, which is fine for restoring testosterone, but not serotonin. This virtual interaction does not give women the hormonal release they need; for that all important oxytocin release and serotonin boost, we need to be around other humans. Think of those times that maybe you have been stuck alone with the kids too long, or maybe you are going through a rough patch with your partner, and it all starts to feel too hard and too heavy. Then you meet up with a girl friend, have a good heart to heart, and suddenly it all seems manageable again. That's because you've restored your hormonal levels, and have the energy to cope once more.

Creating this circle time is essential for women's health. Having regular bonding sessions where we can open our hearts and share with our sisters is not a luxury, it is a necessity, if we want to have plenty to give to our families and our work. I would recommend that we work it in on a daily basis if possible: maybe you get it at the school gate, at the gym, or maybe you are fortunate that you have female relatives living close by, but if you don't have any kind of community that you interact with on a daily basis, you need to go out and find it, for your own sanity.

We live in a testosterone-fuelled society. It's a very competitive world, and the female values of co-operation and support, ironically, aren't supported or valued. This approach also creates stress for women, and I feel it complicates our relationship with money. Traditionally masculine jobs tend to be more testosterone led, ie directional. Testosterone fixes on a goal and doesn't let up until it's achieved its aims. This is easier to quantify financially, which is one reason why men's jobs tend to be better paid. Oestrogen, the main female hormone, is about caring and support, and as these don't have such tangible results, it's easier to devalue women's work.

"Juggling family and work while caring for my elderly mum, and then dealing with her subsequent death, was enormously stressful. You are trying to please everyone, and feeling that you are going to fail." **Jacky**

Plus there's the dopamine factor – as we've mentioned, men are more likely to get a feeling of completion and fulfilment at the end of their working day, while women are less likely to experience those hormonal rewards. So women are less likely to be fulfilled by their day, and still have a need at the end of it to seek further rewards and validation, while the man is more content to rest and ready for the next day. We can see how the unhealthy cycle perpetuates in a relationship, where the woman is looking forward to her partner being her outlet, while he is looking forward to peace and quiet!

To avoid burnout, we need to do two things: make steps to get our needs met on a daily basis for our own health, and ensure the people around us understand how important the work we do is. We cannot expect the people around us to validate us, that is an unreasonable pressure. But we can validate ourselves and then express to the world what that inner validation looks like.

I feel as women, we have to invest a lot of energy just in maintaining our position, whereas men don't have to. I feel I spend a lot of time defending my right to do things differently, to do them in a way that is more feminine - more intuitive, more emotionally-driven. I also spend a lot of time defending my space and defending my right not to bow to the many demands of life. I have to keep trying hard to re-assert that I don't want to take on endless responsibilities, without regard for my health and well-being.

64

Now I have learned boundaries, and learnt self-care, but honestly, I learned the hard way, by taking myself to the verge of a nervous breakdown more than once. Now I put a lot of energy into looking after myself; making sure I get time to myself, trying to do something relaxing and fun every day (not just at weekends!); making sure I get enough sleep; making sure my priorities are ordered according to what pleases me, not just what makes other people happy at the neglect of myself. I have learned to say no to a request that makes me feel uncomfortable, rather than doing it at the expense of myself, in order to not disappoint people.

All this can be quite exhausting in itself! Because I am going against the grain of what is expected of me, what is provided for me. I have to carve out these spaces and these rights, because they weren't there for me before. I have to work to defend them: against the people who want me to take for granted or devalue what I do. ***I am very intolerant of judgement and criticism, and I realise this is because it takes such a huge amount of effort just to be here, to show up everyday, to hold a space of love, compassion, grace, and support, in a world that is low in all these things.*** The amount of people who push, who speak rudely, who behave unkindly. I think it is worse in London than a lot of places, to be a woman in London is tough. To remain graceful, poised, warm, and open, in this kind of urban environment demands a lot of attention.

What Is Depression?

So let's examine what a depressed state looks like for us as individuals. Think about how you feel when you feel down. Really take time to go into it, because our instinctive reaction is to block it out, dismiss it, and act like it never happens. It's a defence mechanism to prevent ourselves from accessing that state too readily. Look at it and don't be scared, because you can know it's not you, it's just a set of biochemical impulses reacting to your environment. Our natural state is bliss. Depression is essentially a sense of hopelessness, of futility. It's the idea that the things that are important to us are impossible, and our life is instead full of all the things that we don't want. It's a sense of overwhelm and fatigue. Ultimately, I think, to turn it on its head, depression is just unexpressed joy: positive energy that is frustrated by circumstance.

"Relationship problems make me depressed because I care and want to resolve issues and everyone to be happy."

I think the most important thing is not to blame yourself! Depression is almost always a result of living in a world that values material possessions and status over happiness. Make the change within yourself. Reprioritise your days to include more of the things that make you happy. Find the people who will support and accept you as you are.

Personally, I am someone with lots of natural energy. I need to feel I have a big purpose ahead of me to feel excited and motivated. I need to have lots of things to do to feel fulfilled. I start feeling depressed if I can't express this natural energy, if it's being blocked either by a dominating person or a stagnant situation, I feel this energy rise up in me with no outlet and I quickly get frustrated and impatient. The longer the period of time goes by without finding an outlet, the more depressed I am likely to get. So it's important to me that I create situations where I am going to be able to express myself: if it looks like I am walking into a scenario where that's not the case, I turn round and walk away wherever possible. You shouldn't be scared of honouring your needs to yourself.

For a long time, I was more worried about letting people down than I was about doing what I really wanted. I would honour the situation, and try and squeeze myself into something that didn't really fit, rather than honouring myself. The deal is though, the universe loves it when you have the courage of your convictions, that's when it really responds best. When you do what you think you have to, the universe is going to keep presenting you with that scenario until you learn your lessons. When you free yourself, then the universe colludes with you in that liberation, and presents all kinds of new opportunities for you to test out this new part of yourself. I don't want to make it sound like depression is self-inflicted, because I know when I've felt depressed how very real and unquestionable it feels. But I want to give you hope and help you understand the small but significant steps that can start to lift you out of your depression. Putting your happiness first can be hard after years or even decades of doing otherwise. It can involve major life changes that might take years to implement. But once you start on the road of making those changes, however impossible they might seem at first, you will start feeling lighter and your depression will start to lift.

Most crucially, you need to lift yourself out of a materialistic self-image. Your worth is not tied up with what you look like, who your friends are, how much money you have, how big your house is, how flash your car is, or how exotic your holidays are. Your worth is integral to you, and it can't be taken away. If any of those things are troubling you, take your mind off them as much as you can. Direct your thoughts away from them, towards the things that inspire you and give you joy. ***Know that you are enough, just as you are, without doing or having anything.*** If you can't believe that, then keep reminding yourself until you can. Keep telling yourself until one day, you will have a wonderful epiphany and realise how majorly fantastic you actually are, yes you yourself are incredible, and how ridiculous everyone else is for not realising it.

I truly believe bliss is our birthright. When we are aligned and empowered, our natural state is bliss. Bliss is what we are. Take on board the principles of a holistic lifestyle, and bliss becomes more and more of a way of life. And the magic of it is, that just moving towards our bliss brings more bliss. Something in our cells responds when we are headed in the right direction. Information about our destiny is encoded deep within us, and when we are fulfilling our destiny our bodies and minds unconsciously recognise that. When we are acting out of alignment, we can't find the peace that we seek, and dissatisfaction and depression will take over.

Bliss is a state nearly all of us know as children, and something we become more and more disconnected from as we become self-aware and learn to wear the masks of our tribe. The tribe teaches us that authenticity and integrity are not the primary values of life, and although our hearts say otherwise, we build up layers of egoic self-defence which distance us from that state but keep us at one with the tribe.

Then something happens, sometimes it's an internal trigger but more often it's external: a health issue, a relationship issue, any kind of issue that makes us feel stuck and blocked, and we decide to reverse that path, peel off the masks, and shed the ego skins. We realise actually it is a greater thing to be at one with the all that is, than at one with our peers. And although it can be problematic to split from the group, the impulse to find wholeness from within overcomes the impulse to collude with the consensus viewpoint.

Each time we dissolve a false reality, each time we dismember an unnecessary construct, we come closer to this state of authenticity we call bliss. Ecstatic bliss is not dependent on externals, it is not attached to a possession or a person. It is a state of joy that is independent of the twists and turns of fate. It is the only thing - apart from this body that we borrow for a life - that we can ever truly own. Because, when you wake up in this state, you know it is yours for the day, no matter what life is going to throw at you. And you recognise, as the conscious co-creator of your reality, that you have constructed it all and the challenges are gifts as much as the joys. It's through the challenges we learn and grow and shed skins and come closer to our own essence. A challenge is merely something we perceive as difficult or even impossible. But as miracles abound and in truth everything is possible, these difficulties are presented to us to help us get closer to the divine miraculous and help us deconstruct our rigid and stuck belief systems.

So I am very clear about what ecstatic bliss is not - it is not attachment to externals, it is not dependent on perceived good and bad or interpreted right and wrong. But I always felt a little vague concerning what ecstatic bliss actually is. And last week I had an epiphany.

68

Something else I write and talk about a lot is the relationship to the self. That our relationship with ourselves is the only one that truly matters. That this work is about cultivating a love relationship with ourselves in the same way we cultivate a relationship with a pet, a child or a lover. It's something we have to work on, maintain and put daily effort into. You don't wake up one morning and think, "Now I know I love my pet, I don't need to feed her anymore." Or, "Now I am married, I can stop bothering to be nice to my partner." (Although that last one is maybe not strictly true and why so many marriages break down!). It's the same with the cultivation of self. You don't think: "Now I can do yoga, I don't need to practice anymore." It's a deepening experience which gets more fulfilling the longer you continue and the more effort you put into it. When we engage in detoxification practices, we never get to the point where we can say we are "detoxed" and we can stop now and go back to cigarettes and alcohol.

To my mind, this cultivation of self is the real point to being here, the main purpose of human existence. And last week, although it seems glaringly obvious now, these two ideas fused for the first time. This is where we find the bliss! In the love relationship with the self. For the more we love and trust ourselves, the more we maintain this core of peace and bliss no matter how the storms of life toss and turn us. As we learn to accept the hard and the easy with equanimity, when the moment passes, we can reflect on our behaviour with approval and contentment.

When we are equally happy with the way we respond when we are in a crisis, and the way we behave when things are going our way; ***when we can stay centred when people are hostile towards us, and stay centred when people are showering us with praise, then we have it.*** We have placed ourselves within the internal conversation, which is to say we are recognising the divine being which we house, and are honouring, respecting and elevating that being. Placing that conversation at the heart of everything that we do is the surest way to ecstatic bliss. And depression at its most basic, is when that internal dialogue breaks down.

It's vital that we don't take on too much or expect it to happen all at once. Big changes might need to be made, but in your fragile state, you won't be able to handle anything major. Be patient with yourself and keep taking small steps in the right direction, allow the process to guide you. The journey is always incremental.

Everything in life is there to teach us something, and even the seemingly hardest and most upsetting situations have a jewel of a gift at their heart. Depression is no different. Depression is a signal from within that big changes need to happen, and when we start to make those changes, depression starts to lift. We are taught to see stress and depression as failures of the individual, but I would say it is the opposite: stress and depression are healthy responses to an unhealthy environment. They are the body's way of communicating something that our conscious minds might not be detecting. See depression as a strong and healthy response that will guide you towards identifying those external weaknesses, rather than identifying yourself as weak and the rest of the world as strong and healthy. Like most things in our current system, you have to turn it on its head to see it for what it is.

Summary

- The main hormones connected with mood are serotonin and dopamine. Women are much more likely to have low serotonin than men. Traditional women's tasks do not tend to be dopamine producing because they are less goal-oriented.
- The odds are stacked against us as women, we are more likely to be overlooked and undervalued, and so more likely to suffer with depression.
- Society is constructed in a way that doesn't support female hormonal balance, and that also makes it more difficult for us to stay happy.
- Our hormonal cycles make us changeable, which makes it even harder to get our needs met, because they can vary so much from week to week.
- Depression is not a sign of failure, it's a healthy response to an oppressive situation. Depression is energy that can't find a place to flow. Don't blame yourself for not being able to feel happy.
- Know that your depression is there to show you that you need to change your life situation, and taking small steps in the direction of your goals daily, will slowly but surely relieve the depression.
- Find what brings you bliss and prioritise it in your life. Seek out affirming and validating work and relationships, and don't be scared to walk away from people who don't value you.

Relationships

This is my favourite part of the book! I love to talk about men, it's my favourite topic of conversation. When I get together with my girlfriends, what's the juiciest part of the conversation? It's when we get to talking about men. Men are so interesting!

It was also the hardest part of the book to write; I wanted to make sure I was writing about commonly experienced patterns between men and women, and not getting confused by my own stuff. At the moment, I'm happy in my relationship, and I can't emphasise enough how I believe that's come from this clarity of understanding the differing hormonal urges between men and women, and how we need to respect and appreciate each other's patterns in order for the relationship to be healthy. I'm not looking to change him, nor am I trying to change myself to fit to him, and that's probably a first for me.

One caveat though: This is written for women who date men. Even though there are some broader learnings about being empowered in relationships, if you're not interested in dating men, you may want to skip this chapter.

Hormonal Differences Cheat Sheet

You probably remember that men produce more testosterone and women produce more oestrogen, we learn that in school. But do you know what that really means, in practice? Bearing in mind everything we've learnt about hormones so far, about how much they provide the unconscious direction and focus for everything we do. This means, quite literally, that typically, men and women have different drivers and focuses. Not only different in fact – opposing. Like gravity and levity, night and day, we are quite literally the yin and the yang of humanity. Just the fact that this needs exploring shows how out of balance we are. Imagine a world where everyone ignored the night-time and tried to create a 24-hour day by keeping everything running all night. How exhausting would that be? That's just an indication of how against the grain we are running this show, and how hard we are making it for ourselves. I believe if we gave more regard to these biological differences, and respected the female drive and focus as much as we respected the males', our society would be in a much better place, and life would flow with more ease and harmony.

We have covered a lot of this already, but for the sake of clarity, let's remind ourselves of the hormonal facts of life.

Key Hormones for Men

- **Testosterone** is directional. Male energy moves like an arrow, moving forward consistently and reliably. Female energy on the other hand, is cyclical, it moves in waves. Women have our monthly micro-cycle, as well as the lifetime macro-cycles. No wonder men find it hard to understand us and call us irrational. In their world, there is no need for these ups and downs, these changes of mood. Testosterone is up and down, but like a lift, not a roller coaster. When it's on its way up, it's on its way up, and you shouldn't interfere with it. Same when it's descending again. When women try and push against men's natural testosterone rhythms, it's like them telling us not to be a bitch when we are PMSing. It really doesn't help! We know it's important to go with how we are feeling, and it's not healthy to repress it. In the same way, although they might not be able to express it well, they instinctively know that it's not healthy to try to redirect testosterone. The testosterone is what we find attractive, but we can't expect them to be on a testosterone high all the time. I think as women, we often fail to understand and respect how testosterone works, and that creates problems in the relationship. We can end up nagging him and expecting him to be at full power consistently, but it's vital that men get their cave time, to go inside and recharge. Testosterone is a law unto itself, just like you are not in control of your oestrogen-progesterone cycles. So it's unfair of women to expect that men can just switch it on when they want him to.

- **Oxytocin** (as we discussed on page 14) is the hormone of bonding, produced during pregnancy, breastfeeding, cuddles and sex. **Women need to produce oxytocin to feel relaxed.** If we don't produce enough, we feel stressed, whereas if men produce too much oxytocin that stresses them out. If we produce too much testosterone we feel stressed! That's why you can only go for so long being a boss before it starts to wear you down. The hormones that relax us, stress men, and the hormones that stress them, calm us. We need to engage in opposite activities in order to wind down at the end of the day. We need to find the ways in which we can wind down, and then come together, ready to give each other the best of ourselves. This was something I learnt intuitively from my first marriage, but John Gray's book Mars on Ice, Venus on Fire is a truly brilliant look into these opposing hormonal drives.

- **Serotonin**, if you remember, is much lower in women than men (plus men rebuild it much more quickly), and the main activity that boosts serotonin production is talking – so women literally need to talk four times as much as men! At the end of a hard day, or in times of stress, women normalise by talking – it literally makes us feel better. Whereas at the end of a hard day, men need cave time – talking is the last thing on their list. Testosterone is solution-orientated; men need to go away, come up with a plan, and return like everything is fixed. By talking about it, we seem to be making it worse. Whereas to women, not talking about it is part of the problem! Our serotonin levels drop, and we start to worry even more. This opposite way of dealing with problems (and stresses in the relationship), I think is one of the biggest issues between men and women – not understanding how we have instinctively opposite ways of solving problems. It's one of the hardest thing to achieve this communication balance, to allow both these instincts to co-exist and be equally valid in the relationship; you need to allow his silence, and he needs to allow you to feel heard. When you find someone whose patterns match yours, you've found a keeper. Allow him his cave time as long as he needs it, and instead of worrying about what he is doing and thinking, focus on your own process. Then, you can both see more clearly where you are in that when he comes out of his cave. Don't seek reassurance from him, seek it from yourself, and then see if he is able to reflect that confidence back to you.

- **Oestrogen** is the most well-known female hormone. Oestrogen controls our monthly cycle, and its rise and fall is what makes us changeable and unpredictable. It's the caring and nurturing hormone, that makes us put others' needs before our own. Knowing your cycle is really key in knowing yourself, and also within your relationship, to make sure your man knows where you are in your cycle, so he knows which of your many heads you have on – are you channelling your inner Shakti or your inner Kali? Men make small amounts of oestrogen, but I believe it's key that men avoid commercially produced dairy products, as this can increase their oestrogen levels to a point that makes them less driven. For the same reason, women can find their PMS improves when they cut dairy out of their diet. Small-scale, organic raw dairy products are more easily tolerated, but mass-produced products contain unhealthy amounts of oestrogen.

Hormones in love

Sexual intimacy between two people releases a whole host of chemical reactions in the brain. Women release oxytocin, which makes them want to bond and to cuddle. Men are depleted in testosterone, which makes them withdraw and go quiet. Understanding this interplay made things so much clearer for me. After intimacy, it felt like I was in love, with all these new chemicals rushing around my brain. In order to justify and to keep creating this hormonal high, a woman starts to construct a story around the guy she has just been intimate with. We think of all the reasons why he would be a good match. We fantasise situations, like going out for dinner, him meeting our friends, travelling somewhere exotic, staying in hotels, even having babies and getting married! We ignore all the reasons why it might not work or he might not be suitable, because these hormones make us feel good, and they need a reason to exist. When the sex is good, it's too easy to overlook all the attributes in him that would drive you crazy in a long-term relationship. So in his absence, while he is off in his cave, we need to manufacture excuses as to why we can keep getting high off these hormones. We find patterns, and we see signs, because we want so badly to manifest those. Little things remind us of him, maybe we see someone wearing the same designer label as him, or we hear a song we know he likes, or we see someone who looks like him. Our primitive hormonal drive is on a mission to create connection and this is such a strong and ancient impulse, it totally overrides the cold hard facts of the situation.

For the guy however, it's a different story. The loss of testosterone leaves him feeling depleted and empty. He must go out into the world, and achieve more, do more, make more, in order to feel full and strong again. He needs to move away from you, so that he can come back to you. Women, in their lack of understanding of the differing hormonal experiences, can feel that as rejection, but for men, that pulling away time is essential to their health. To limit a man at that point is to diminish his masculinity, which is not what we want to achieve. So it's a very delicate hormonal dance that goes on. Male hormones and female hormones take us in opposite directions, and it's an incredibly intricate manoeuvre to get them to synchronise. That is actually love! When both the woman and the man can allow their hormonal cycles to flow freely without either feeling diminished or compromised by the other, but instead feeling empowered, attuned. And this is why a relationship is a practice that demands awareness and attunement, not something you can enter into and then be disengaged about.

This also helped me understand how to let go of trying to control relationships. A few years ago, there was a guy I really liked, and I thought maybe he liked me. Should I invite him out for a juice next time he was in town? I asked on FaceBook what people thought. Did it work if women made the move first, or is it like the books say that men need to make the move? It was a very popular post, with dozens of different answers. The one that stuck in my mind most was my friend Anna, who simply said, "Never never never never never."

*"I find it hard to pinpoint how to breakthrough to the male ego without actually punching them in the face. It's the language they know, so that is what they want - but I'm not gonna go that route." **Anon***

I still wasn't sure though. It took a few more guys who went nowhere, to make me agree wholeheartedly with Anna. I believe that the happiness in relationships directly springs from how much we feel free within them. It doesn't matter what you do in your life, in fact I would say that for women the more assertive and in control we need to be in our work, the greater the need for us to be able to express our femininity in our intimate relationships. Your partner needs to be totally committed to you, and to making you happy, and if any part of them needs to be coaxed or persuaded into the relationship, that's not a strong foundation.

Learning that was an enormous release. Previously, I always felt like I had to let a guy know I was interested. I had to give him hints, reassure him, let him know I was available. In doing so, I made myself vulnerable, and open to getting hurt. I was also prolonging the torture of not knowing if it would go anywhere. It's so hard to turn your attention away from a prospective partner when your oxytocin is raging, but that's what a goddess does. Her focus remains on the universes within and maintaining their delicate balance. She doesn't need to do anything to push the relationship in any direction: if it's not flowing of its own accord, it's a waste of her effort. It's much easier for a man to do that, because he doesn't have the same primal hormonal drive to loyalty. To walk away from a relationship in order to preserve his energy for his work, his career, his betterment makes much more sense to him. Women topple at the first sign of attraction, and fall into a massive state of imbalance, which ends up being unattractive, and working against us. If we can see through our hormonal urges as a kind of madness then we can avoid putting ourselves in situations that are at best embarrassing and at worst soul-destroying. It was an incredibly hard pattern for me to overcome, but not giving into my hormonal impulses, walking away from insecurity and remaining true to myself as an empowered woman, is ultimately immensely validating and rewarding in the way a weak and insecure relationship will never be.

What Is Attraction?

To maintain a successful relationship, I believe we have to remember that old adage, "opposites attract."

If we go for a partner who is similar to us in terms of energy, an equal balance of masculine and feminine energies, it will feel very safe and familiar, and easy. But the passion, the dynamism that keeps the relationship driving forward will be missing. So much of the time people create other drivers to stay together – children, or a home, or a business – and the partnership may endure but the romance that we crave dies away. This is what many people of my generation settled for: it provides stability, it fits with the status quo, but it's not necessarily the kind of love that will move mountains.

Because of the difference in brain chemistry that motivates our life choices and that we base our decisions around, men and women approach the world from different vantage points. We can be literally living in different worlds. And ironically, that's where the attraction lies. If someone can see things and approach them in a way that feels out of our range, then combining forces with that person makes us more powerful. The attraction comes from the sense that the other has something we don't have, and that having that thing will make us stronger. The attraction is in the mystery, is in the not-knowing, is in the expansion that will occur. The greater the mystery, the deeper the attraction.

That's how attraction begins. But how does it go wrong? If you are a strong woman, with a surety in your femininity, and strength in your intuition, you will be attracted to a high performing man who is busy achieving great things in the world. The chemistry will be amazing. Fireworks will blast from every chakra. You will feel complete and you will feel powerful and you will feel like you have made it. And then you know what? He does something that is utterly incongruent with how you see the situation. He will destroy the magic, seeming to throw away what you have. Your actions are stimulated by oestrogen and oxytocin; his are stimulated by testosterone and dopamine. The very chemicals that brought you together will drive you apart if you do not understand that they will always be in opposition.

This is why men and women need plenty of time apart. There is, as always, the occasional exception that proves the rule, but usually when I talk to people in successful long-term relationships, spending big chunks of time away from each other is a crucial factor in keeping the fires burning. You need to accept that your partner can only make you happy some of the time, and the rest of the time you get on with your own lives. The more dependent you are on yourself for your happiness, rather than the other, the smoother the process.

This is easier said than done when oxytocin is in the mix! Oxytocin can hold on for months, even years. And love produces an oxytocin/dopamine rush which is one of the best highs there is, and highly addictive. We can find ourselves acting like crazed junkies trying to get another hit of those love chemicals. We do things that are out of character, in order to keep mainlining that oxytocin. But this is destructive behaviour. We have to realise how oxytocin impairs our judgement, and learn better how to analyse the situation objectively. The objective reality is that the man you fall for is going to have plenty of traits that you do not understand or maybe even particularly like. The fact that you don't understand him is good! That is why you are attracted to him, so wanting him to change is not the answer. Being less focussed on his personal development and more focussed on your own trajectory is.

We are taught in our culture to externalise. So when we enter a relationship, we have a tendency to see the mission as being to reform our partner. We see potential in him, and we want to facilitate that expansion. But this is the fatal error that causes the relationship to go off track. We must always make our lives about ourselves. The mission is always to reform the relationship with self, to expand the self. When we keep that as our focus, and make the relationship serve that focus, we cannot go wrong. When the relationship becomes the focus, and we put our own self-development aside for the sake of maintaining the relationship, we are heading for trouble. Because the universe needs expansion, the universe always seeks to enter new territories, and anything that blocks and hinders that cannot last.

I feel like women too often blame men, when it is just as much our fault for acting out of disempowering beliefs, and not in accord with the natural laws of our energy. We are not used to holding power. It's far more familiar for us to give it away. So once we feel comfortable in the relationship, we happily start acting out the patterns of our mothers and grandmothers before us, believing that that is what women do. Understanding the hormonal impulses helps us understand why we feel like we do, but then it also helps us rationalise that behaviour and act on it appropriately. When we don't understand why our hormones direct us to behave in certain ways, we say, "Well this is how I feel. It must be real, it must be true. This is what feels right to me." Whatever you feel, however strongly you feel it, won't change the fact that the object of your affection is not obliged to feel things in the same way. And if we want to build successful relationships, we have to understand that yes, our feelings are valid, but also, they are exclusive to us. And then use that understanding to build bridges between our heart's desire - which is to be enveloped in a safe, lasting and fulfilling love - and the reality of the male experience, which has a greater need for risk, detachment, and space.

Actually, I believe this blind spot in women makes us too often oblivious to the single most important factor in your relationship: how he treats you. This is the make or break element. When all is said and done, this is what really makes you happy or not. Not how funny, handsome or clever he is, what his job is, who his friends are, where he takes you, what he buys you, or any of those externals. He could be super successful, talented and rich, but he's not going to make you happy unless he treats you like a Queen. Oxytocin is created by attention, remember. Every girl needs to feel like she is important to her partner in order to be happy. If he doesn't make you feel that way, it's no go. Yes he needs his space to do his own thing, and it's important to honour his boundaries. But the stark fact is, if he's not attentive to you, you're not making oxytocin, and you're not in love.

80

For him to stay in love, he needs to keep producing testosterone: he needs to keep chasing. *For you to stay in love, you need to keep producing oxytocin: you need to feel wanted. It's that simple. The more wanted he makes you feel, the more in love you will be.* It is this single factor that creates the polarity between you and drives the relationship, and without this, you don't have it. Love boils down to a highly sensitive hormonal interplay. It's a dance between testosterone and oxytocin. He has to leave you, but not for too long or you will go off the boil; you have to be out of reach, but just a little bit or he will go off the boil. If there is an imbalance on either side, the relationship palls. I believe that's what chemistry is: a delicate interplay where his rhythms match yours, and the distance he creates feels reasonable and still adequately meets your emotional needs.

What pressure we put on each other in relationships! We all have this idea of the fairy-tale prince or princess who will make us complete so we can live happily ever after. How much responsibility is that for any person! It's crazy behaviour. We have to learn to make ourselves happy. To expect that someone else will do it, and then to blame them and resent them when they don't, is very unfair of us. We all know women tend to be better at emotion. So why would we expect that he can not only deal with his own emotions, but also take on ours? It doesn't make sense. *When we deal with our own emotions, we are strong, dependable and attractive to the right kind of men. While we are looking for someone else to untangle our mess, we will attract men who are stuck in equally unhealthy patterns and will just mirror our own back to us.*

After one particularly painful relationship breakdown a few years ago, I sought advice from a wise male friend. I wanted to understand better how and why men shut down, and can disconnect from love, when this process feels like torture for women. He helped me to understand that it's the disconnect from the emotions that is actually the real torture. He said that

81

as women, we see it as we are the ones who are suffering, but it's better to feel the pain and to be able to move through it than not feel it at all. Before that conversation, it seemed to me that men had the advantage in being able to cut ties more easily, but now I see it as the other way round. I understand that I am likely to have increased emotional empathy than the man who has captured my heart, and not to expect either that he will match that empathy or even understand it. By acknowledging my emotions but not assuming that he will be able to recognise them, I can remain strong in my power despite the tumult we might be going through.

"It can be challenging for him to understand my processes with things, or how I feel so strongly about things that can't be seen, but it's simply because this is something he, himself is working on. As he really is very intuitional and is in the process of cultivating that so it's that it isn't a regular experience for him yet. So it's just another way for ego not to get in the way of taking things personally or feeling like one has to defend or prove something, and to continue to be compassionate toward the places we are individually, and learning from each other the value of each perspective and approach." **Tania Marie**

Men are Chasers & Women are Choosy

Guys love to chase. The dopamine and testosterone the chase produces excites them, it charges them up. So they see a woman and they chase her. Guys who are not in long-term committed relationships can be very good at this part of the game. They see it as an art, and they get a lot of practice.

Women are more choosy at this stage. But women love to be chased. Few women get enough intimacy and connection in their daily lives. Women need more intimacy and connection than men and our modern world is not set up in a way that makes it easy for a woman to get her needs met. So most single women welcome the attention from a man they find attractive, and this in turn fires up her hormones. Plus, one of the major stressors for modern women is how to survive financially. It doesn't matter how emancipated you believe you are, it's a harsh fact of life that women are lower paid than men (at the time of writing, it's nearly 20% less), and it's a difficult financial climate to be single in, whichever gender you are. So whether she realises it as a motivation or not, finding a partner is going to take the stress off financially, to a degree at least. Add to that the biological clock ticking somewhere, however distantly in the background, and you can see why generally women have a greater urge to seek out a committed relationship than men do.

Men are thinking short-term. Men have a goal in sight, and that goal is you, and it's going to give him enormous amounts of satisfaction to get you. Women naturally think longer term, they are thinking about building a home and raising a family, so they are a lot pickier at this stage. But the more she is chased, if it's done with style and charm, the more her hormone levels are raised, and she is persuaded into thinking seriously about this guy. She will be painting those pictures of their life together and trying to assess how he will fit into that picture and how happy it will make her. This releases oxytocin and serotonin, and makes her feel good.

If she can construct a solid enough fantasy image of their life together (and it's so important to remember it is just a dream at this stage, however real it may seem in your head), then she will allow herself to be caught. Depending on the variables, this could mean anything from an initial date, to a one-night stand, to a romance that lasts a few months. But at some point in the dance, she stops doubting him, and she decides to put her trust in him.

At that very point, something in him shifts. The hunt is over. For the first time, he looks beyond the preliminary chase, and considers the future. Men are programmed to spread their seed and dominate the tribe with as many offspring as they can muster. His default is to move on once he's caught his prey. His primary urge is now to leave you, it is not to start thinking about life-partners.

Women in this position are blinded by their hormones. This oxytocin high makes it hard for them to think rationally. To them, they are at the beginning of something momentous, something they have been waiting for for a long time, something they have been saving up a lot of energy for. All the reasons they doubted him initially have fled their minds. She knows love conquers all, love knows no obstacles, and she loves him so they will resolve any issues. He, for maybe the first time, is now the one behaving rationally. I think at this point, men can actually see much better than us who is suitable as a long term partner, and we should thank them for that. When they reject us at this point of the courtship, it doesn't make sense to us, because we were ready to "give it a go" and "try and make it work". But men are much more instinctive in this department, and in not trying, they are actually saving us months or even years of wasted energy and eventual heartache.

So let's just recap. The guy gets his high from the chase. Once the chase is over, the testosterone high is over. For a man, maintaining high testosterone levels is everything, it's what gives him the lead in life. So he's going to exit, rebuild his testosterone, and try hitting on another girl to get the same high again.

The girl gets her high from the bonding. Initially, she's cautious about opening those hormonal floodgates, but the guy persuades her it's safe to do that in ways he has mastered over the years. So she opens up, and at that minute, the guy backs off, leaving her desolate and confused. She would never do that! Create intimacy and then so abruptly destroy it. It's a behaviour so foreign to her nature, she makes excuses for him. She keeps reimagining the fantasy in her head, trying to hang onto that oxytocin high.

He doesn't consider that he did anything wrong. He almost certainly didn't mention any future plans. He wasn't talking about moving in together and having babies! He may have charmed you by telling you how beautiful and special you are, not like any other lady he's ever met, and how much he was into you. He didn't say anything about a relationship though, did he? He didn't, he really didn't. So the woman is left feeling that the fact that this isn't going anywhere is her fault, because she obviously read far too much into it, and who would want to be with a desperate kind of person like that?

The man moves on, hormonal balance intact, the game played according to his rules. The woman moves on, hormones a mess, blaming herself, confused, rejected, the game played according to rules she doesn't fathom, and so she reasons she must be at fault somehow.

84

I believe it all begins with the lack of community in our culture, and the way women are subtly devalued. We are taught to work work work and what happens outside of work is just a way of getting over yesterday's work and ready for tomorrow's. The feminine traits of sharing, nurturing, holding space, trusting, loving, caring do not have enough value placed on them, neither monetarily nor status-wise. So women are fundamentally starved of the oxygen they need to be happy. And that gives men a power, because when they give that intimate attention to a woman and see her light up, they have power over her.

A happy woman, a woman with bundles of oxytocin and serotonin and dopamine to spare, is a powerful woman. Suddenly her immunity shoots up. It's a fundamental prerequisite for the dynamics of a successful relationship that the man must have greater immunity (see next section). He cannot have her too powerful. So to ensure the survival of his genes, his primal self must put her down by rejecting her, making sure she knows her place and he is still holding the power. A man needs to find a woman whom he can make happy but not too happy; if he sees that you are happier than he has the capacity to handle, something in him will want to sabotage it.

Sisters, we need to dig deep. We need to be strong. *We need to value ourselves so we don't look to men to give us value. We need to understand our own hormonal dance so we don't get so swept up in it. We need to never chase a guy; as soon as he shows signs of non-committal, we need to step away, and back into our self-knowledge.* Remember that you are an incredible goddess and a blessing to any man, and the right man will know that and will pursue you and make sure you know that, and if he doesn't do that, he's not your man. When we are strong, we attract in empowered men who are on the same path of self-examination, so together we can navigate into a new space where the relationship is not playing out according to the old paradigm power dynamics. And we never needs to go out looking for this man, because we know that we draw him in by the power of our inner magic.

Have you ever had a thing for a guy and then he goes off with a girl who, to be honest, doesn't seem a patch on you? Do you ever look at a girl who seems fairly average and wonder how she ended up with such a catch of a guy? It's because men are attracted to women who are weaker than them. Men need to dominate. And it doesn't matter how liberated and open-minded they are, a strong woman is threatening to them. She is not attractive.

On a biological level, men are programmed to spread their seed. Their overriding drive is to fertilise as many women as possible, to ensure the survival of their genes, and dominate the gene pool. Women on the other hand, are driven to stick with one guy as a protector for their children. While pregnant and breastfeeding, she is very vulnerable, so she needs to make sure someone is looking after her in order to make sure her children her raised healthy and happy. So right there we have two opposing genetic impulses to ensure the survival of the species: the urge to be with many women versus the urge to be with a single guy.

Another biological factor to consider, is that men are looking for strong women, who are going to make the best babies. A woman who is fit and healthy is going to deliver more babies and raise them to be productive adults who continue the species. While a woman is looking for the guy with the best genes to pass onto the next generation. The woman wants the strongest guy she can get. If she is stronger than the guy, he is worried she will leave him, so to be safe, he needs a woman with strong immunity, but just a little bit weaker than his, so he can dominate. It's a very sensitive balance: too strong and she will reject him, too weak and he is not creating optimum offspring.

Suddenly, both the Alpha male groupie syndrome and the Alpha female can't-get-a-man syndrome are all too obvious. How many successful men do you know, leaders in their field even, who can't settle down? Who objectify women continually, and work their way through them mercilessly? The stereotype of the rock star with his new groupie every night is very much a reality, because a guy is attracted to any woman who is genetically weaker than him. That gives the Alpha male a huge pool of women to draw from. And a bottomless pool of willing victims who find him attractive. He can basically get about any girl he sets his mind to.

The Alpha female however, is only attracted to men who are stronger than her. If she is super healthy, that's a very small selection of men. And those men are likely to be all off swimming in their infinity pools, with no incentive to create a lasting bond with a woman. So many incredible, beautiful, talented, intelligent women are single these days, and I believe this is why. That's not to say she won't find her guy eventually, because there is a magic involved that goes beyond basic genetics. But the odds of society are stacked against her, and whereas it's easy for a guy to have fun until he's ready to settle down, a woman tends to focus on her career and herself, being much more work-driven, because there are less options available to her. She might well be attractive in an ideal way, but in terms of guys actually trying to engage with her on an intimate level, pickings are slim.

We forget that so much of the process of attraction is down to this interplay between our physical bodies, and how our genes, not just our conscious minds, are sizing each other up to decide if we are a match. As your saliva mingles, you are firing off tons of signals conveying how your genes match his. As he touches your body, his mind is making unconscious assumptions about your fertility, and your chances of carrying his offspring. I believe one of the most crucial factors that determine whether we remain interested in a prospective partner is this primal and unconscious interpretation of the intermingling of our physicalities.

A study in 2013 (by Elizabeth McClintok, if you want to look it up), showed that the more successful the woman, the less likely she was to be having casual sex. Because a successful woman knows she can get what she wants, and what a woman wants is more likely to be a long-term committed relationship. So the conclusion of the study was that, "for women, the number of sexual partners decreases with increasing physical attractiveness."

The accessibility of contraception has also worked against women in terms of forming relationships. When the chance of getting pregnant was very real, women had to be much more careful about who they hooked up with. By removing this barrier to casual sex, it's enabled us all to explore our sexuality more fully and freely. But it's diminished women's power in relationships, as that selectivity was our ace card. We have traded the role of being the chooser for the freedom to also be the chaser, and it muddles the picture. The end result is that women become less of a precious commodity, and easier to manipulate according to the testosterone drives. This is why I believe the Tinder culture is deeply unhealthy, and inherently unsatisfying for women.

One night stands are just not an easy option for women the way they are for men. Firstly there are different hormonal impulses occurring (testosterone vs oxytocin), which put men and women in very different states after sex. But more importantly, for women to thrive, she needs to concentrate in on herself, focus on building her inner resources, so she can attract in that mate, that partner that does stick around, through the power of her own inner magic. Dipping in and out of other guy's swimming pools is just diluting her energy.

Understanding this principle helped me realise something which I really wish I had understood as a young woman. We are cyclical, but men are directional creatures, and they need consistency, so casual sex suits them because it helps them to get their sexual needs met continuously. Women's energy moves in waves, and it's natural for us to have a pregnant phase before the intense energy of birth, that is, a monogamous period to allow time to create the right conditions for the next relationship. I think we are taught to measure ourselves by a standard that suits men better, and to see being a single woman as some kind of a failure. Our culture has an unhelpful tendency towards short-sightedness, rarely does it take the long-term viewpoint. *In all the "How to Get a Man" dating books I read while researching this book, not one mentioned the benefits and positives of taking a sabbatical from men: instead we are indoctrinated*

to make ourselves always available and desirable. I wish I had been taught from the start that a fallow period is a necessary precursor for a woman to create the fertile soil for a healthy relationship. That making myself the focus of my attention and cultivating my inner magic for as long as that took was the real way to get my heart's desire. For a woman, being single for an extended period is not a failure, it is a wise move that will ensure her a man of a high calibre.

Intimacy

To understand modern day relationships between men and women, we have to frame them within the wider context of our culture. And in doing so, we can understand better how we are being let down. The world we live in has become increasingly competitive and cut-throat. For the last few decades, it has valued independence over community, financial wealth over emotional wealth, and fame over integrity, although I perceive a shift starting to happen as people realise this is not an optimum way to live. For women growing up in the 70s and later, we were taught that our life's path is to get an education, find well-paid employment, and work until pension time. The traditional female roles of homemaker, mother, and life-partner, are given little or no precedence. We are expected to work those in around our busy successful careers. If we adopt this inherently male definition of how to create our lives, we do that at the expense of the authentic female experience.

Women have a much greater need for community and intimacy then men, and we are often lacking in nourishment because we are not getting as much bonding and close connection as we need which leaves us stressed and depressed. If a woman is in a full-time job, and going home to a place where she does not have an intimate connection, with family or a partner, then she is going to be deprived of the elements that she needs in life to make her hormonally balanced and well-adjusted. It might seem from the outside that she is in a successful career, doing well with a nice home, but biochemically she won't be happy without the necessary support groups in her life.

So this is the key premise that relationships begin from. It's a man's world. Men are likely to be far more comfortable within the structure of their lives than women. The majority of women are gasping for air. The attention of an attractive man is like oxygen to her. A woman comes into a relationship feeling she has so much to give that the world doesn't see. She is looking to step into herself, and offer herself to her man. She is ready to open up a part of herself that the world doesn't allow her to express in her day-to-day life, but that she needs to express in order to feel whole, to feel like a real woman.

I don't know that most men realise this. I don't know if they recognise the gift and the honour it is to have a woman open up to you in this way. I don't know if they have any idea of the amount of love and light that can flood their world if they allow in a good woman. I think maybe men are taught to value this need for expression as a weakness. Rather than allowing a woman to step into her strength and power, they view the act of her trying as desperation in itself. Why is she not simply happy within herself, like he is? Men will view women as needy, attached, clinging rather than recognising the beauty in what she is attempting, maybe a little cack-handedly, to offer. And women find it difficult to see how a man does not need that connection as much as she does, so she cannot comprehend it when he backs away. To her, it's like being offered a gourmet dinner when you haven't eaten in days and then only being allowed one bite. Why would he want to take the plate away?! It makes no sense to her. While he, if he is an attractive, successful male, will be feasting like a king as much as he chooses. He fails to see why she is so hungry, and in fact her savage appetite makes her unappealing to him.

If men understood truly how much an evolved woman has to offer, and how denied she is of that in her every day life, I don't think he would pick her up and discard her so lightly. But he is taught that exploiting women is acceptable in the name of pleasure, in fact he wouldn't even recognise it as exploitation. Of course, we also need to consider the behaviour of women who have been damaged, are less self-aware, and who in their weakness try to manipulate men; these kind of situations help support the man's viewpoint that a woman is just out to get what she can from him. A weak person very often turns into a bully given the opportunity. I know many men have had experiences of this nature and those experiences then give them cause to dismiss women in general as creatures ready to disempower them and drain them of their male energy.

So then we have the current situation, where men are always on the defensive, which puts women on the offensive. This is a reversal of our natural positions, and I don't think we can put this right until women themselves learn to operate out of a place of power rather than using their victimhood as a means to bully men. *As women we need to restate our boundaries and our limits from a place of wholeness, and show men how rich and fulfilling healthy relationships can be.*

To See and Be Seen

As the traditional roles slip away, we become increasingly muddled about what relationships really are and what they mean to us.

A young western woman nowadays does not need to find a man for all the reasons her mother or grandmother might have married. She can provide for herself, she does not need a provider. She can create her own purpose in life, she does not need a man to define her. She can find companionship in her friends. She can look for sex online. Why does she need a commitment to one man? It's possible she will think of her parents' relationship and not have positive healthy role models. She might well think of men who don't communicate well, who bring tension and anger into the household. She could well remember her mother being unhappy in the relationship a lot of the time, but choosing to compromise and put up with that. It's easy to see why she is not going to seek a man for a long-term relationship and instead follow her own path, her own dreams.

But something still nags, something is still missing. What is it that we still seek? I would venture that missing factor is intimacy. We can have a successful career, and be valued in our work, we can have a happy home and be loved by our friends and family, we can be financially successful and secure in life, but without an intimate relationship at the heart of all that, there is still a gap, a hole.

Intimacy is physical, but it cannot be found in a one-night stand. Intimacy is an emotional bond, which builds over time. Intimacy is letting someone in behind the mask that you show to the world. Intimacy is seeing and being seen.

Why are we so obsessed with selfies? Because we want the world to see us the way we see ourselves. So much of the time, the vision we have for ourselves is at odds with the way the world views us, and we desperately want the two to align. We want the world to know who we are, we want to project our mark onto the world, and not be defined by the daily mundanities that rule the lives of most of us. In our modern lives, it feels like us against the world. Our hearts, our dreams of freedom, are pitted against the caged reality of work, commuting, chores and all the other resented necessities that fill our days.

When we find intimacy, someone is taking our side against the whole of the rest of the world. Someone else is agreeing with our viewpoint, seeing as we see, colluding with us on what reality is. Without this ally, the world can seem a lonely place, however many friends we have. We feel things are a certain way, it's how they appear to us, but the rest of the world seems to be telling us we are wrong by not seeing them the same way. We want one person to be in accord with us, to agree with us that we are a good person who deserves the best in their life.

The concept of a soulmate is so popular because we want so badly to be seen. We can go through our daily lives feeling invisible – to the people we live with,

92

people we encounter on public transport and in shops, people we work with, it can feel like no-one really sees us. We want to be seen the way that we see ourselves. We dream that if one person will see us that way, then everyone else will as well. But you know who the only person that really has to see us is? Of course, it's ourselves. All the times the world seems against us? That's really us, getting in our own way. When we think we are not strong enough, not beautiful enough, not amazing enough, not important enough, the universe will keep testing us until we finally admit how strong, beautiful, amazing and important we are. Every lesson that comes from the universe, comes with love. We have to accept the universe's love fully, and then it will come to us in human form, as a reflection of what we already know.

The universe cannot bring to us what we can't see. If we want someone to see us, we have to see ourselves first. If we want intimacy, we need to be fully intimate with ourselves, not hide parts of ourselves away. I wish we were taught this at a young age. I wish we told our children that they will live to a long ripe old age and there is no rush to find a soulmate. That they should learn how to see themselves, that the relationships that they need and deserve will always come, and the pursuit of anything else is a distraction.

"I get on with what is right for me, then things with him and others naturally work out. I think we are designed to operate as individuals, dedicated to our dreams, then love, romance, attraction etc., just fall into place." **Holly**

Giving Your Partner Your Best

In the monogamous, death do us part situation, we are taught to accept our partners for better or for worse. When I was younger, I thought your man was someone you could feel comfortable being totally yourself with, warts and all. Nothing wrong with that in theory, apart from in practice it means dumping all your shit on someone. No wonder they go off us! No wonder rifts start to occur in the relationship. If you are dumping all your baggage on someone and asking them to deal with it, that's not attractive in the slightest. Not in this day and age when we all have so much more opportunity and choice.

When I fall in love, it's because I think that man is incredible. He blows my mind with his talents, his charm, his charisma. He melts my heart with his tenderness and affection. In my eyes, he is a god. Why would I want to dump my shit on a god? Nope. I wouldn't. I want to give him the very best of me. I want to work on myself even harder, and take care of myself even better, so I can give him the true pure love I believe he deserves. It's a sacred union, not a battleground. If there's something I don't like in him, I need to look at myself and see what I haven't dealt with that means that he is reflecting that in my life. I need to take some time to myself to work on that and then see if we can come together harmoniously again. Blaming or judging him for his perceived failings is never constructive, and trying to get someone to change to suit you is not a strategy that is generally proven effective!

This, to my mind, is a key part of the paradigm of empowered relationships. We do not need a partner to bestow on us status or wealth, because we get more satisfaction out of doing that for ourselves. We do not need them for validation or to stop us feeling insecure, because we have learned that we can do that much better than anyone else could. We want to be with them for the pure joy of it, the pure bliss of that intimacy and mutual adoration. If we aren't depending on them for material and emotional support, then it's vital that we carve out that time to do that for ourselves. We must come to our partner from that place of wholeness, in order for the adoration that we seek to flow.

Time apart is so key, so we have something to bring to the table. For previous generations, a woman who lived with her man day-in day-out, had less to offer as her experience of life outside the domestic sphere was so limited. So she was easier to take for granted. If we do not want to be taken for granted, we must meet him in an empowered place, and we can only be empowered when we have invested the time and energy in ourselves. Thus men fall into their natural place in our lives, an essential place, but not an overriding place; rather than how things were in the old paradigm, where we put men at the centre of our lives and then couldn't fathom why he wasn't making us happy.

I think I was brought up to believe that if I was dissatisfied about something, if I felt someone had wronged me, I had a right to express that as "my truth." I saw my truth as an objective fact that another person needed to take on board in order to make me happy. Now I know that all truths are subjective, and that everything I experience in life is through the lens of the relationship with myself. If he is doing something that I don't like, of course it's important that I explain why I'm not comfortable, but I don't have a right to expect anyone to change to please me! If I take responsibility for all negative emotion myself, rather than directing it at someone else, then I have two options. Either I deal with my own emotions, stop blaming the other person, and instead thank them for allowing me insight into myself. Or if I don't feel it's helpful to deal with those emotions – maybe I haven't got the resources right then, or maybe I'm being pushed into a negative space I feel isn't healthy – then I can distance myself from the relationship and spend time with people who make me feel good about myself. Either we are getting along, or if we are not, I can leave – but I shouldn't expect anyone to be anything other than what they are. Even if we think we are trying to "fix" them somehow, staying in the relationship to help them, like it's for their own good, that's not a healthy situation to be in. People never change when we are trying to make them change, acceptance and gratitude are the keys to change. If we can accept someone as they are, and be grateful for who they are, then we are truly allowing them to grow.

Different Rules For Love and Work

The dating industry in the USA alone is worth $2 billion! Today's woman is confident and liberated and believes she can go about getting what she wants out of her life. But when it comes to relationships it seems very apparent that we don't know what we want, and I think that's because we have misjudged what will truly make us happy. I have no doubt when we figure out what really makes us tick then we can achieve it. But even with all our new-found strength and power, when we attempt to operate the same way in our relationships as we do in our careers, and take the same principles of independence and control, we find ourselves failing drastically. We are single when we don't wish to be. We end up dating one asshole after another. We enter relationships only to find them oppressive and dysfunctional.

I believe everything in life is a spiritual practice. Eating. Breathing. Sleeping. Moving. Thinking. Working. I try to approach everything I do as a way to connect with the divine and expand my essence into the world. I try to be conscious around every thought, word, and deed. And relationships are no different. We have to approach them with a whole new framework of understanding. A Michelin starred restaurant chef needs a different set of skills from a raw food chef, even though they are both dealing with food. A gym instructor needs a different set of skills from a yoga teacher, even though they are both training the human body. An empowered woman is a relatively new phenomenon in our culture, and she needs a different kind of relationship from her mothers and grandmothers who seemed to exist more readily in disempowered relationships. She needs a new set of skills to navigate and nurture this relationship. We cannot simply take the old rules and apply them over our new lives, no more than a traditional gourmet chef can switch into raw prep without any attention or effort.

For an empowered woman to have a successful relationship, she needs to give it the level of focus and energy that she does her career. Not the same kind of energy, mind you, but the same level. She shouldn't expect it to come easy or naturally. She shouldn't expect to feel like she knows what she is doing a lot of the time. But she should know that she is carving out a new template for healthy relationships, and that it will take a lot of faith and trust in the process. To her children and grandchildren, the strides forward she makes will seem obvious and completely natural. But at this point we are making baby steps into a new paradigm for relationships, and that's not going to feel or look like dating did in the last century.

I think we have to look at relationships completely differently from how we look at the rest of our lives, and that's not to suggest that we are splitting ourselves into separate compartments, and denying parts of ourselves. It's to say that we are finding a relatively unexplored and unchartered part of ourselves and we must be very delicate and sensitive around that if we want it to thrive.

The relationship between me and myself must remain central. As soon as I make the relationship between him and me more important, then I've lost.

96

Everything is about the relationship with self. That is what pulls a man to you. Your relationship with your man can only be a reflection of your relationship with yourself. Focus on that, and you will draw in the perfect man. If your primary focus is on him, then you are using him as a way to avoid looking at your own insecurities. Only you can make you happy. Learn how to make yourself happy, and attract a man who reflects that. Depend on him for your happiness, and not only is that unfair, it doesn't work!

And know who you are. If you don't know who you are, how can you know what you want? And if you don't know what you want, how can you ask for it? Knowing who you are is central to the success of your relationship. Don't let your man define you, and then blame him for not being able to define you in a way that makes you happy. You need to be able to stand apart from him, independent, sure in yourself and your happiness, just as you are. John Gray says, the woman needs to make herself happy, and then the man can make her happier!

Courtship Circuitry

When you're in a relationship, it's like you're rowing a boat together. You've both agreed to get in the boat with each other, and that's pretty exciting in itself. It's usually the man who starts off doing the rowing, and the woman is flattered and delighted by his attention and strength. Before too long, he needs a break, and she sees that it is her turn to row, gladly taking up the oars. All too often, this is where the relationship fails! Having punted off from the shore, the man feels his work is done. He is happy to sit back and let her carry on the rowing for as long as she can. He may, when prompted, pick up the oars and do a few strokes just to show willing. And the woman keeps rowing, knowing that if she stops it's all over, and they will have to get out of the boat. In her desperation to stay afloat, she will drive herself to the point of exhaustion, while he, enjoying the ride, barely notices anything is wrong. Sound familiar, to an extent at least? So how can we as women make sure we are not doing all the work in the relationship? Well, you won't be surprised that the answer comes back to hormonal balance.

Love is one of the greatest highs known to humans. When our brains flood with these chemicals, rationality goes out of the window, and we will do anything to keep getting that fix. The main effect of the drug cocaine is it causes the brain to release dopamine in large amounts – the high from love can be even stronger than the high from cocaine! It's dopamine that gives us that delicious but wired feeling – unable to eat, sleep, or focus well, but bursting nonetheless with natural energy.

Oxytocin, as we've discussed, is the other hormone responsible for sending us screwy with love. Oxytocin gives us that feeling of oneness with another that we are all seeking. Pair the two, and it's easy to see how we can become obsessive about getting close to that person so we can get more of that hit. We want to feel giddy with desire, that sense that we've finally found something that's more important than all the mundanity and bullshit that we put up with most of the time, so we feel compelled to take all kinds of risks to be with that person. We want to feel that sense of closeness that lets us know that we are not alone in this world, a world that is cold, harsh and individualistic to a point that crushes our oxytocin. It's why the Free Hugs movement came to be, but at the same time seeing a group of people standing in the street offering oxytocin looks a little absurd. When our world desperately needs more oxytocin flowing, to stand there offering it randomly to strangers actually becomes a radical act.

So we know about dopamine and oxytocin by now, but this is where it gets interesting. When a man orgasms, he releases a surge of dopamine, and the knock-on effect of this is that a hormone called prolactin is released. As dopamine dips and prolactin rises, that hormonal combination makes him irritable and depressed. If we are not aware of this hormonal cycle, then he will naturally have a tendency to blame his partner for his post-coital lows and withdraw from the relationship. This is the basic idea of Tantric sex – that delaying orgasm will short-circuit the dopamine release and therefore avoid the emotional drop.

Prolactin is really just nature's way of making sure we don't all become sex addicts, such is the power of the dopamine high. This helps us to understand why intimacy can have the opposite result from what we intended: that dip in dopamine makes both parties feel that something is out of balance with the relationship. And if we don't understand it as a natural biochemical shift, then it would seem all too clear that it must have been caused by our partner! Practicing Tantra will ensure that the man's dopamine stays in more even rhythms, and stop him disengaging. The problem is compounded because the dopamine low can make the guy feel stressed and depressed over the relationship, and that makes it even harder to get back to the oxytocin high that the early days of love creates.

Don't Be An Enabler

"I nourish myself by saying yes when I mean yes, and no when I mean no. I know what I want." **Louise Hay**

In researching this book, I spent a lot of time looking at popular literature. Books and videos with cringe-inducing titles like How to Get the Guy or How to Catch the Guy or The Secret of What Men Want. There is a glut nowadays of books telling women how to behave in order to get her man; not so many on telling men how to behave to get their woman. They mostly start with the revelation that yes, men are different from women, and you can't expect them to act like your girlfriends. This is a relief to us all, the first epiphany, if you like, and the shared ground that gets us turning the page. But from that basic premise, they all take you off on different tangents, which to my eyes are just a myriad of different ways of enabling men in their dysfunctional behaviours. It's so important to know your value, and put that before anything else. When preserving the relationship becomes more important than your own personal happiness, you know you have become an enabler. It's so bred into us to allow men their emotional incapacity, and find ways to tiptoe around that in order to keep the peace, but we don't need to do that anymore. We need to make the stand, and appreciate that loneliness alone is much healthier than loneliness in a relationship. When we are lonely alone, we can look at that and change that. But when we are lonely in a relationship, there is someone there preventing us from being honest with ourselves, and moving forward with our self-development. Instead we are using their dysfunction as an excuse to mirror our own unwillingness to evolve.

We have to understand men's different ways, yes. And we have to know our value. But then we put those two things together to be able to call them out, gently and lovingly, when they are not acting in alignment. Not bend ourselves out of shape just to fit in with them. That does not do us any favours, or them. Stand tall, and let him rise with you or not at all. Shift the paradigm: women are the ones who are used to putting themselves in a position where they feel they are not enough as they are. Instead, let him know that he is not enough, but in a way that is empowering to him. When men let women know that they are not enough, it's done in a way that diminishes, in order to keep us in our place. When a woman can communicate to a man that his behaviour is not hitting the mark, she can do it in a way that gently allows him to become enough, to step into his potential. This is the power of a goddess, she holds space to allow a man to evolve into his fullness. This is what your man wants from you! He actually wants you to put your foot down, and help move him out of his dysfunction. The world revels, celebrates and even rewards that imbalance towards the male energy, in a way that pains us all. A man needs a woman who can see through that, reach his heart and soul, pull them out from under the layers of programming, and ask him to shine wholly on a daily basis.

Because we've reached the point where we understand why his behaviours are different from ours, doesn't mean we need to tolerate them. It's not about learning how to deal with men so that we can stay with them without getting so upset, as the books would have it! It's about seeing how easily they disconnect from us, and by remaining in our power regardless, gently showing them a way to come back into alignment with themselves. **All those Get the Guy books are missing the true point of the feminine aspect, which is to pull in, not to chase, catch or get, but to attract in. As soon as you are chasing, you are losing.** Step back, the goddess always steps back, leans into the universe, knowing that it in its infinite wisdom will support and take care of her, better than any one man ever could. She does her yoga, breathes, cries or smiles as she wishes, but she doesn't disconnect from her feelings in order to stay connected to her man. She embraces her feelings, the pain as much as the ecstasy, and trusts where that will lead her.

Women have a tendency towards empathy, so that when the relationship starts going wrong, our habit is to think about what he is going through, think how he is suffering, and do what we can to make sure he isn't pained by the experience. Our false assumption is that he will do the same for us, but this is rarely the case, men handle pain much less well than women, so he will readily accept your support while being unable to offer any in return. This happens all too easily when we put aside our own process for the relationship, and allow the relationship to dominate our internal landscape. A woman who has kept in touch with her process, who has allowed that to remain at the heart of her life, will not be blinded to her own pain in this way. She will have a healthy sense of self-preservation, and so rather than immolating herself on the fires of love, she will step away from the flames and not get burned. She may still be empathetic to his pain and his struggle, but she will not let that distract her from remaining true to her own wants and needs. In other words, she won't take that shit. This is not disengaged, this is actually true compassion – to feel another's pain but not see it as a responsibility or a duty to fix it. Only he can fix himself, and you can be there for him as a guiding light and a space holder for that process.

Patriarchy harms men as much as women. It prevents men from having a space to explore their emotions and expand into their heart centre just as much as it does us; it's just they are outwardly better at coping with it and carrying on with the day-to-day, and remaining apparently successful despite their emotional shutdown. They need us to have a strong emotional core, and thus be a healthy reflection of their own ability to connect to their emotional body. We are more naturally connected to that, and we must cultivate that for ourselves as much as them, rather than mirroring their own shutdown behaviours.

- Men's and women's hormonal needs work in opposition. Don't expect your man to think like you. Don't try to think like him.
- Never chase a guy. Do your thing, and if he is the right guy, you doing your thing will be crazily attractive to him.
- Know that your hormones make you crazy. That oxytocin-dopamine rush is one of the most powerful natural drugs on the planet. You are high. Enjoy it, but don't get carried away, try to stay connected to your rational self.
- If he makes you feel insecure, it's not healthy. Your guy will make you feel like the most amazing woman in the planet.
- Women need more emotional intimacy than men. Get your needs met from your girlfriends, family, pets or in your work, so you are not always desperate for his attention.
- Be financially independent so he can't assert dominance that way. Maintain your independent status, no-one is worth giving that up for.
- If your guy is not the one leading the relationship, it won't work for either of you. He will feel emasculated and resentful. You will feel drained and tired out.
- Never compromise. Stick to your guns. Always stay a little out of reach. He wants you to make him work for your love, that's what excites him.
- Women are programmed to monogamy, men are not.
- Women are programmed to seek out alpha males, men are not programmed to seek out alpha females.
- How he treats you is the most important thing. Not what you have in common, his status, or his wealth.
- How you treat him is just as key. Give him your best because that's what he deserves, and don't use him as a dumping ground for your undealt-with shit, that's just not kind. Of course, it's inevitable at times but that doesn't make it right.
- Know that you are navigating relatively un-chartered terrain by being an empowered woman in a healthy relationship. Don't expect it to be straightforward. Don't play by the same rules you use in the rest of your life. Love is a package to delicately unwrap, not another of life's

battlefields to be conquered.

- Understand the dopamine-oxytocin high that is the beginning of love, and learn ways to sustain it so love doesn't fade away
- Don't be an enabler. By refusing to accept a man's shutdown behaviour, you give him permission to evolve, which is actually what he is seeking.

Monthly Cycles

Tracking your cycle is a vital tool for staying in touch with yourself, and understanding your mood changes better. It fascinates me that this rhythm goes on in our bodies for decades, and most of us pay it little attention. If you are anything like me, you will have a vague notion about how your moods and energy changes every month, but until I got into hormone research, I genuinely couldn't have told you anything specific. The book that really educated me on all this was Women's Bodies, Women's Wisdom by Christine Northrup. This is a women's health bible that if you don't already own, you really should.

The information below may be very school textbook to some people, but perhaps that's also why it's forgettable? So it bears repeating.

Ovulation occurs after a build-up of oestrogen in the system, midway through our cycle. If an egg is not fertilised, then it is shed, and that's what we call menstruation and the beginning of a new cycle. So far, so facts of life. *What's important to understand is that the first 14 days of an average 28-day cycle are all about the oestrogen. The second 14 days are all about the progesterone, and these two hormones have very different effects on us.*

Oestrogen, which starts everything off, means elevated serotonin, which in turn means positive, happy thoughts! Oestrogen makes us feel confident and outgoing. Nature is programming us to go and find a mate. The first week, you may feel a little weak still because of the blood loss that comes with menstruation – particularly if you are low in iron and magnesium. Your energy and vitality peaks in the second week. Once you ovulate, oestrogen starts to drop, and progesterone rises and peaks just before our period comes. Progesterone makes us feel more inward and need to nest. We are likely to get more sensitive and aware of our unmet needs. Biologically, we are preparing for pregnancy, and need to feel safe and loved, or we can get cranky. Week four is the hardest, and we are most likely to feel dissatisfied with life. If you feel like having it out with someone – a work colleague or a family member for example, check where you are in your cycle first! If you're in your fourth week, be aware that you are unlikely to feel as heated about the issue in a week's time. Sometimes it's beneficial to capitalise on this energy, and get a difficult truth out that you have been suppressing, but it's also worth considering waiting a few days, so you will be able to express yourself in a calmer and more constructive manner than the Kali, destroyer of worlds, vibes you were feeling while you were premenstrual.

When oestrogen is high, this is the time to make the most of your confidence – go clothes shopping, hit the gym, go out partying. If it's at all within your control, plan big events (like first dates, job interviews, public speaking events, weddings!) for that second week of your cycle. When progesterone is high, it's the time to stay in and nest – get out the chocolate, read an inspiring book, stay with people you know well and can be intimate with. This is the time to catch up with girlfriends over Skype, book a spa treatment.

Of course, I'm not suggesting that you put your life on hold for half a month every month, but it really does help to be aware of these cycles within ourselves and plan our schedules in a way that is supportive of our needs, rather than goes against them. I do yoga wherever I am in my cycle, but I know that during last few days before I menstruate, I'm more likely to find it a strain and then I don't beat myself up about why I didn't do such a good practice. It helps us to understand why one week we are madly in love with ourselves and our lives and the next week has us wondering why we are such a failure, when nothing much has changed! If progesterone is inclined to make you feel more dissatisfied with your life, it's so helpful to have an awareness that nothing will feel as bad next week. That's not to say you can just ignore the dissatisfaction, it's still necessary to look at ways in which you can use that to make changes in your life, but it just helps to get perspective on it.

I think this is one reason why women don't suit the 9-5 as well as men. We have weeks when we can be incredibly productive and feel like we can conquer the world. Then other weeks when we need to slow down and be more receptive. Men need that receptive time as well, and I don't believe they get enough of it in our current "always-on" culture. But women need it much more, and I don't think it's healthy for us to have to always be in our masculine, always getting shit done, in the way society demands of a modern career woman. That's going to cause a build up of stress which is eventually going to get to her. Hence the proliferation of Western middle-class women who get to their 30s and decide to quit the corporate rat-race for a more balanced life as a yoga teacher or massage therapist, with a schedule that permits them walks in the park with the dog, and mid-week afternoons for shopping and catching up with friends.

Recently in Bristol, a company called Co-Exist made the news for granting their female staff "Period Days." They are allowed two days off in the month, as long as they make up the hours at another time in the same month. This to me makes total sense. When my energy levels are high, and I'm soaring, I'm happy to work into the night, with the satisfaction of being on a roll and knowing I'm getting the job done. When I go into my more receptive phase, I'm more interested in reading, researching, and getting an early night, and it feels a strain to have to switch into output mode. I'm fortunate that I work for myself, and I have reached a level of security that allows me to follow my cycles more intuitively, but it wasn't always that way.

"As soon as I educated myself on my cycle and who I was in those four weeks, and learnt how to harness the power or powerlessness, I felt less stressed. The menstrual cycle is a wave, and we need to master it." **Linzi**

Remember, men's energy is directional. It's like a lift, it simply climbs steadily, reaches a peak, and then needs to descend again to gather energy for the next ascent. Women's energy is cyclical. We move in waves, it's a more curvaceous, undulating flow, and much harder to predict. Think of a mosquito coil. It may seem to men that we go all around the houses to get somewhere, while for us it looks like they take one step forward and two steps back! It's just different ways of working, but actually, we get to the same point at the same time. Men go from A to B to A and then back to B. Women go from A to B but in a very roundabout way. The 9-5 suits men, because they can make their ascent in the daytime and the descent in the evening. But women need larger chunks of time spent in one mode or the other. When we are in oestrogen mode, the quiet times that men require can seem limiting, and when we are in progesterone mode, the busy days that men demand can feel like too much. So if a woman is not careful, she can feel like she is always swinging from one extreme to the other – from finding her life unfulfilling and dissatisfying, to finding it overwhelming and exhausting. All this can add up to a general malaise and sense that nothing is ever right. A woman who is aware of her cycles, can tailor her diary to meet her needs. A woman who is out of touch with her cycles will be blaming those around her for not being able to cater for her ever-changing demands, and creating dissatisfaction in her relationships and career.

This is another great example of how our culture is structured to suit the patriarchy. Imagine how the men would cope if it was the other way round, and they were being forced into rhythms that went against their nature. They would make such a fuss! I would say that most women struggle to surf the waves that are set by male energy, but we are unlikely to make a fuss about it, and instead internalise it and see it as a failing somehow. As we enter the digital age, we will increasingly find ways of working that can accommodate both cycles, but currently it's still the women that suffer with lower paid jobs, and more stress and depression issues.

Ovulation is literally when you are at your peak – it's when you are most confident, fertile, ready and open to life. The time when you are feeling most attractive, is also the point where your sexual desire is strongest, and the signals your body is giving out are most appealing to men. Nature is doing everything it can to make sure you have babies! Having done everything it can to help you conceive, nature then assists you in keeping the baby – by making your energy go more inward, and your sexual desire lessen, so you are less likely to act in risky behaviour that could harm the baby. If no baby comes, then bam! The cycle starts immediately over again, to maximise your chances.

Men are not hostages to their biology in this way. It's probably the biggest, single most fundamental difference between us. For a good 30 years or more of our lives, these hormonal surges really control us and dictate how we plan our days. For a woman not to know where she is in her flow, is so fundamentally disempowering. We have to know what sets us apart from men, so we can be at peace with that, and express it in constructive ways. If we are trying to be like them, operating in a routine that doesn't ebb and flow, but stays static and constant day in day out, we are going against our very biology, and that can only cause stress.

The easiest way to track your cycle is by measuring your body temperature. If you take your temperature first thing in the morning, every day, you can quickly start to see a pattern. Your body temperature rises the day after you ovulate, and remains higher until menstruation. Ovulation to menstruation is a pretty standard 14 days – it's the menstruation to ovulation part of the cycle that can vary a lot from woman to woman. So knowing when you are ovulating is super helpful for several reasons: you can anticipate a shift in your energy and mood; you can understand when you are more fertile and use it to help either try to conceive or avoid conception, and you can fairly accurately track which day your period will start. It's also just fascinating to observe these changes in ourselves physically, and gain a little insight into how our biology affects our psychology. You might also want to use one of the tracking apps that are available now, such as Hormone Horoscope. You put in what day of your cycle you are on, and it gives you insights into how your hormones will be affecting your moods and energy levels.

If you find your monthly cycles are out of whack, and affecting your mood and energy more than is manageable, there are two hormonal areas that are well worth examining. If you haven't guessed, we're going to come back to our old friend, cortisol, and also insulin. Cortisol, the stress hormone, is the one that messes up all the others, remember? If you've got underlying stress issues that are troubling you, e.g. the obvious worries about money, or relationships, then this is likely going to have a knock-on effect and make your PMS worse. It's the body's very clever way of looking after itself. If you insist on sweeping the issues under the carpet month after month, they will only build up into something chronic. So this time of reflection every month is an opportunity to learn how to manage your stress levels with mindfulness and meditation.

Oestrogen protects against insulin resistance, so in the second half of our cycles, when oestrogen is lower, we are more likely to crave carbohydrates and sugary foods. If we want to balance our insulin levels, it's important not to get out of control around those cravings.

Essentially, the first part of our cycle is when we are feeling more attractive, and the second part is when we are more reflective. Having these dual aspects to our nature is what makes women complex and dynamic creatures. Understanding how our own inner pendulum swings, and creating a lifestyle that fits around that, is essential to our happiness. If you have had a balanced upbringing, a secure childhood, and are now living a materially comfortable existence, it's unlikely that your pendulum swings will be that wild. But for anyone with any undealt with trauma, or living in stressful situations (ie, most of us), not being in touch with our cycles is just going to increase the sense of stress and disconnection we feel. We are taught the biology at school, but not the psychology, and it would be so immeasurably helpful to have this information at adolescence: a solid understanding of a shifting situation.

I feel it's so ironic that it took me most of my fertile years to really get to grips with this rhythm: when you're caught up in it month after month, it's very hard to stand outside it and observe it with any perspective, and it's only now it's coming to a close that I have the space to look at it in a way that finally makes sense.

It's so obvious it sounds a little crazy, but *I think we are encouraged so much to prioritise other things in life over this self-awareness, and tracking your cycle is way down most women's to-do lists.* We wake in the morning with so much to navigate, so many activities and tasks before us, we are not keen to add more. It's a perfect example of how women sideline themselves in order to put other people's needs first. I wish I had really understood the need to prioritise this one, so it could've helped me get the most out of my waxing and waning body.

Because we live in a patriarchy, society rewards the attractive and demonises the reflective. The pre-menstrual woman is seen as a harridan because she sees uncomfortable truths that the patriarchy would rather not confront. The side of you that emerges in this fourth week is in touch with a deeper, more intuitive knowledge than the ovulating female who is rising to the surface, shiny and eager for the world. The key is really in enabling the lighter side of our personalities to create shifts and changes in our lives that suit the deeper side of ourselves. A lot of women use their attractive nature to please others, particularly men, and then their reflective side will ultimately feel displeased with their lot, because they are giving everything to everyone else and not keeping enough back for themselves.

If you use your attractive side to orchestrate your life in a way that works for you on a soul level, then you are winning, and you can have both – appreciation and validation from your inner world as much as your external world. And a winning woman is way more attractive than a woman who is faking it outwardly, and losing it inside. ***When you meet a woman who's got it together, she has a magic about her that's unmistakeable. It's such a rare thing - to find a woman who knows how to orchestrate her light around nurturing her darkness.*** The women our culture holds up as role models are the ones who orchestrate their light around diminishing their darkness, believing that in some way they can extinguish it, not realising that being able to hold the balance at that midpoint between light and dark is where the magic lies. That's the beauty of our cycle: it teaches us to honour both, to know that both are integral parts of the life experience, and we get to own that rhythm in a more deeper and connected way than men get to do. Our cycles have much to teach us, and typically, most of us aren't even listening.

110

Summary

- It's almost universal for women to have a monthly cycle, from adolescence to menopause, which affects our moods and energy levels
- In the first half of the cycle, from menstruation to ovulation, we tend to be more outgoing and confident.
- In the second half of the cycle, from ovulation to menstruation, we tend to be more inward and reflective.
- It really helps to make the most out of your energy to be aware of your cycles and set realistic schedules.
- It helps those around us if we understand how our moods change from one phase to the other, and don't blame others for our altered perspective.
- Use your outward energy to support your inward energy – don't work against your intuitive side, but listen to it and use those times of the month when you're energy is higher and more productive to work towards scenarios that work better for you.
- Appreciate your light and dark, and know that being able to move easily between both is magic indeed.

Raising Children

Raising children is about the most individual yet universal experience you can have in this life, which is why it's so mind-blowing. Your kids - if you have them - are literally an extension of you, the continuance of your DNA, and as such deeply personal, but at the same time you are doing something which is about as basic as being human gets – reproduction. It makes you feel so special and important, having this little being totally dependent on you, but at the same time it's the most humbling thing, being able to see yourself as just another link in the chain of life, in service to this tiny little creature.

My parenting methods weren't conventional, by any means. They worked for us and they worked really well; I'm fully happy with the choices I made with my three sons, and the experience of the past twenty years (and counting) has been wonderful. I feel like I squeezed all the juice out of their childhood, we had so much fun and good times, and I feel I've raised balanced, happy, intelligent individuals who I love spending time with and I think are generally great people. But I wouldn't assume that my choices would be your choices, and accept that most people wouldn't find it easy to do it the way I did it.

Briefly though, if you're curious:

- I long-term breastfed (2.5-4 years each child, ten years in total).
- We co-slept for at least a year.
- I carried them in a sling until I couldn't physically manage it any longer (around a year).
- I raised my kids on a primarily raw vegan diet.
- None of my kids have had any vaccinations, antibiotics, or pharmaceutical medications of any kind, ever.
- We home-educated until 16.

What I would prefer to write on though, rather than prescribing specific parenting methods, is my experience of how it felt to be a mother of small kids, and how the world treated me. Mothering itself was a joy – being a mother, less so. A whole heap of unexamined baggage the world has about what a mother is hit me in the face, and a lot of time I felt like I was wading through shit. Yes, I signed up gladly to loving my kids, educating them, nurturing them, tending to their needs. I did not sign up to becoming a second-class citizen, and a lot of the time, I couldn't work out how to extricate the two.

The women who are given the most attention in our culture are the Miley Cyruses, Taylor Swifts, Rihannas and Nicki Minajs. Young, childless women who trade on their pretty faces and their sexuality. The women who are least important are those whose fertility is no more. Although, thankfully, this is beginning to change, older women are still generally ignored and written out of the story, their voices disregarded. Once I was pregnant, I had the brutal realisation that I too, almost overnight, was out of the running. I hadn't realised how much currency my youth and attractiveness had given me until my body changed shape. I had been a blithe size 8. Suddenly I went clothes shopping and found nothing to fit and/or suit – I hadn't realised how clothes were all suited to a certain body size, and how privileged I had been to fit that image. It's thankfully different now, twenty years on, but at the time I was so angry that I could only buy white maternity bras. Even black bras were hard to find, let alone anything coloured or interesting or remotely pretty. I hate white bras! Why assume that all breastfeeding women don't care about lingerie? Because we had entered the realm of being purely functional beings and were no longer considered playthings. The fact that our sexuality might be independent of our fertility apparently did not register with underwear designers.

Parenting books were another issue. Most start with the assumption that we need telling what to do. I think this is typical of the self-doubt that women have! We've raised kids forever, it's encoded in our genes more deeply than just about any other activity, and yet we doubt our natural instincts and abilities. If we went to a bookshop right now, we could find dozens of parenting books on the shelves, all with different and conflicting suggestions of how to do it. It's rare though to find any books that discuss parenting from the mother's standpoint. As an individual expecting equal rights in society; the only two books that spoke to me were Naomi Wolfe's Misconceptions, and Rachel Cusk's A Life's Work. Both talked about the hardships and disappointments they faced in realising motherhood put them on a new and unexpectedly uneven playing field. The image of the Madonna, the saintly mother sacrificing everything for her offspring is so strongly embedded in our consciousness. It's extremely challenging for women to question this, and ask why, in the 21st century, should that still be so? As women who have been raised to believe that equal rights have been won, it's nothing short of devastating to realise that in fact - a good couple of decades of what is considered the prime of your life - will be ruled by the tyranny of your biology. It's definitely still taboo, to step outside the limitations of the hausfrau, and ask if it's possible to claim more for yourself.

The other book that I adored was Naomi Stadlen's 'What Mothers Do – Especially When It Looks Like Nothing'. A beautiful book, which devotes whole chapters to the myriad of unrecognised and seemingly endless tasks that fill our days, and stop the world falling apart. These were the real issues on my mind: what I did with the kids was something I didn't think about too much, we just played it by ear and it seemed to me pretty obvious. They needed to sleep, eat, play, learn, and there wasn't time for much else really, these simple basic survival activities became all consuming. But the fact that I suddenly became an invisible member of society, perceived as someone who wasn't contributing now I wasn't out in the workplace, troubled me. I wasn't doing nothing; I was working harder than I had ever done in my life! But I received no financial reward, nor did I have the support of a team of colleagues. It was hard to find positive role models, to find public figures to align myself with, who spoke about mothering in a way that was identifiable to me.

My altered role in society was something that troubled me deeply. Before I got pregnant with my first son, I was intending to be a music or fashion journalist. I studied at the London College of Fashion; I interned for i-D magazine. It was a pretty clear path ahead. But with the birth of Reuben, all those doors that had seemed wide open, swung firmly shut. Worlds diverged. I am grateful for the direction life sent me in, because I think parenting was ultimately a far more true and fulfilling experience than I would have found in the fashion and media world, but it was the shock of realising how separate those realities are that got me.

There is the socially constructed world of the media, and there is the guts and glory of what really happens in our lives, and it felt like never the twain shall meet. Plenty of people live outside of that false media bubble, but as one of the privileged few who existed within its narrow parameters, I had never properly taken notice of the yawning chasm between the false image we are presented with and the real lives of most people. And, how that false image imprisons the people that that media was supposed to be reflecting. The ideal woman the media portrayed wasn't a reflection of the women who consumed it; instead it was obscuring the truth, and hiding us from view.

As a mother, I was too busy and too tired to perform the role that had got me so far as a woman previously, but more than that, it didn't seem important anymore. It seemed false and shallow, and I realised all the things I'd been taught to care about, all the ways I'd been shown to channel my energy to achieve success where subtle deflections from the truth. They were paths to sidetrack me from myself - self that in this moment of primal strength, the strength of a mother giving everything to her children, was immensely powerful, and so subversive, that she can only be locked away and ignored, for fear she would remind the childless women in which direction their true power lay. Not as dolls, always sweet, pretty, kind, smiling; but as powerful creators, givers of life, the womb from which men grow, providing the milk by which they are nourished.

Not to imply that being a mother is the only route to empowerment, but that we do not do enough to venerate women when they are experiencing this peak in their powers through motherhood. To acknowledge the true power of the woman at this time would benefit all women with a greater understanding of where their strength lies, whether they are parents or not.

In relationships, women tend to consider the external things about a guy, like his status and career, and how she will look on his arm, but then neglect to give weight to the most important factor – how does he treat me? In parenting, we worry so much about the children and how to do the best for them, we don't look at how the parenting experience is for ourselves. We think, if we are struggling, that must be our problem, our failings. We blame ourselves, and in doing so, we allow these massive injustices to continue to be perpetuated. At no other point in your life are you likely to feel the weight of the patriarchy than when you have children under seven years of age. Because you will have no reserves, you have little energy to win even the most minor victory, and stand up for yourself. Your children are more important, and rightly so, but it leaves so many battles left unfought and the oppressors the clear victors.

Of course, the irony at the heart of this scenario, is that we would be a million times better at being mothers if we got just a fraction of the support we need to receive. These are not selfish demands, as our detractors would say. We are asking for a bare minimum of respect and appreciation for what is undoubtedly the most challenging and demanding period of a woman's life. We need this so that we can create well-adjusted, highly functioning human beings to further the evolution of the human race.

When kids are supported, we get a healthier society

Raising children should be at the heart of our culture. Instead, it is pushed to the sidelines, and we are made to feel an inconvenience and a burden with our extra needs and demands. Finding a place to breastfeed, navigating public transport with a buggy, dealing with a potty-training toddler who needs a wee urgently, making school runs on time with a baby in tow - these are just a few of the daily tasks that become enormous mountains to climb when they take place in a hurried, selfish, irritated world. By the time our children are grown and we start gaining ourselves back, for most women I would guess that it's such a relief to be out of that particular prison, that they would rather not go back and revisit the skeletons in the closet, rake over the old mud. So they close the door on that chapter, and leave all the issues in there, undealt with, for the next woman who step into the room known as "Harried Mothers in a Hurried World," to tackle.

Recently, I received a deferment letter from Student Loans, and I wondered why they wanted to see my bank statements. I Googled it to see if others had questioned this invasion of privacy, and found a long forum thread of dozens of mothers who all had the same problem. Their husbands supported them, so how could they prove their income? They had no independent income, so nothing to show in their bank statements, and they were very stressed imagining that the loan company might be intending to take money off them when they didn't technically have any. This highlighted to me perfectly the different way women experience financial transactions from men. For men the scenario is more likely to be: do a job, get paid, it goes in the bank. For mothers, it might play: do a job, don't get paid, and have to find creative ways to make sure they and their children eat. This right here is the nub of the patriarchy. If we can make women independent at this point in their lives, we will free the whole of the society they live in – men, women and children.

The financial insecurity that accompanies those early days of motherhood damages us all. It damages our relationships, and it damages our children's future. It puts a strain on men as much as women, and affects how unconsciously safe a child feels in the world. This financial imbalance has an emotional knock-on: women acutely feel the weight of responsibility to have these small beings dependent on them, and yet who can they be dependent on in turn? Not all women have babies with a partner who can provide them with the amount of support that they and their offspring need to survive without stress. State handouts are usually given grudgingly, and it's rarely enough. This financial precariousness at such a pivotal time in a woman's life has a deeply scarring effect on her psyche, and it's a wound that she passes on to her children. Supporting the rights of parents to care for their children without fear around survival issues, much higher on our priority list if we want to create adults who feel that the world is a welcoming and abundant place, full of opportunity and possibility,

*"The idea of not being able to cover my costs makes me feel stressed, because it also runs a story that I'm not good enough, and that I'm too old to be having this issue." **Daniela***

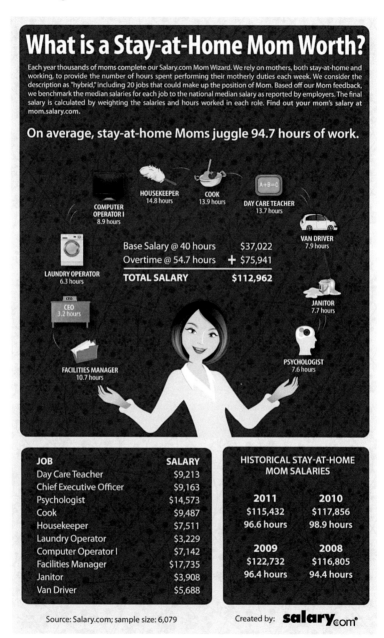

What is a Stay-at-Home Mom Worth?

Each year thousands of moms complete our Salary.com Mom Wizard. We rely on mothers, both stay-at-home and working, to provide the number of hours spent performing their motherly duties each week. We consider the description as "hybrid," including 20 jobs that could make up the position of Mom. Based off our Mom feedback, we benchmark the median salaries for each job to the national median salary as reported by employers. The final salary is calculated by weighting the salaries and hours worked in each role. Find out your mom's salary at mom.salary.com.

On average, stay-at-home Moms juggle 94.7 hours of work.

HOUSEKEEPER 14.8 hours
COOK 13.9 hours
DAY CARE TEACHER 13.7 hours
COMPUTER OPERATOR I 8.9 hours
VAN DRIVER 7.9 hours
LAUNDRY OPERATOR 6.3 hours
CEO 3.2 hours
JANITOR 7.7 hours
FACILITIES MANAGER 10.7 hours
PSYCHOLOGIST 7.6 hours

Base Salary @ 40 hours	$37,022
Overtime @ 54.7 hours	+ $75,941
TOTAL SALARY	**$112,962**

JOB	SALARY
Day Care Teacher	$9,213
Chief Executive Officer	$9,163
Psychologist	$14,573
Cook	$9,487
Housekeeper	$7,511
Laundry Operator	$3,229
Computer Operator I	$7,142
Facilities Manager	$17,735
Janitor	$3,908
Van Driver	$5,688

HISTORICAL STAY-AT-HOME MOM SALARIES

2011	2010
$115,432	$117,856
96.6 hours	98.9 hours

2009	2008
$122,732	$116,805
96.4 hours	94.4 hours

Source: Salary.com; sample size: 6,079

Created by: **salary**com

The nuclear family problem

I also think the nuclear family set-up is fundamentally unhealthy, and where a lot of our problems arise from. It's actually a relatively recent concept. A hundred years ago, marriage was only likely to last a couple of decades, before one or other of the partners passed on. The romantic notion of having a partner to share all aspects of your life with is a recent phenomena; marriage was generally seen in much more practical terms by previous generations, and men and women weren't expected to spend so much of their time together. The idea that one person can be all things to you is a little crazy, when you think of it. You expect this one person to be able to:

- Be nice to you all the time
- Like every aspect of you
- Only behave in ways that please you
- Financially share your responsibilities
- Be your best friend
- Be really good in bed, all the time
- Understand you in ways even your parents didn't
- Co-manage a household with you
- Take all their holidays with you
- Always want to do what you want to do

And so on and so on, I'm sure you have a whole host of your own unrealistic expectations you can add to the list! Don't you think it's crazy, when you consider it? This is just one person. How do you expect them to replace everyone else in your life and be the only person who matters and who never lets you down. It's also pretty much a romance killer. Romance, as we discovered in our chapter on relationships, is a delicate navigation between two sets of hormonal responses. That in itself is a thing to orchestrate, without all these other responsibilities that we insist on putting on another person.

I feel the nuclear family scenario is pretty much doomed for the empowered woman. There is virtually no way it's going to play out in a way that gives her the equal rights and the space that she needs. She must attenuate,

119

and then the strength and beauty that attracted her partner to her in the first place will be diminished, and he will lose interest. She is doing all she can to please, but she can't be enough. And it will work in reverse as well, she has such high expectations of her dream lover, the partner will always feel as if they are coming up short. However hard both parties try, however much love there is between them, the situation is stacked against them, and it's no wonder that it's rare the couple who comes through the other side of raising children with their partnership intact.

The Ways I Felt Disempowered as a Mother

- Lack of sleep. Hand on heart, I swear I didn't get an unbroken night's sleep for ten years, and most of the time I was managing on four or five hours sleep a night. This completely messed up my cortisol levels, and meant I was permanently running on empty. Not a healthy situation, and not one in which a person feels capable of making calm, considered and thoughtful changes in their life.
- Ten years of breastfeeding meant my oestrogen-progesterone balance was completely out of whack. Pregnancy and breast-feeding is like permanent low-level PMS. You are much more likely to be cranky and over-sensitive, less confident and assured. All your energy is going into protecting your children, and you don't have much left to protect yourself, so you become very vulnerable.
- Lack of financial freedom. This is a big one. How many women can maintain financial independence throughout this period in their lives? Very very few. So in male-female relationships, the man becomes more powerful.. Most couples nowadays wouldn't consciously buy into this scenario, but the reality is that the man becomes more dominant and the woman becomes more insecure as the financial power shifts in his direction.
- Lack of time to yourself. Time alone is essential for gathering and centering oneself, restoring energies. Self-care is an important practice for us women so we can give what is expected of us in the world. When my third child was a baby, I got one hour off a week, to the minute, and that lasted for the first year. For the second year, I got two hours! I was empty. I barely knew who I was anymore.

- The huge emotional adjustment a woman makes in transitioning from a girl to a mother. You are quite literally becoming a different person, and while this internal process is taking up so much energy, you don't have so much for fighting the external battles.
- Less time to concentrate on your appearance. Like it or not, people take a well-groomed, fit and healthy person more seriously than they do someone who is less well turned out. If you have had four hours sleep and baby sick on your last clean outfit, and no chance to take a shower because the baby has been demanding all morning, you have less credibility in the world than the woman in lipstick and heels.
- Likely to not feel as confident in your body. With all that breastfeeding, lack of sleep, extra eating for the baby, and lack of time for exercise, you are not going to be at your most confident, and you might feel more like lurking in the background for this period.
- Less likely to feel sexy. Women have great sexual power over men, this is no secret in our culture. But it's less likely that you will have this valuable currency in the bank at this stage of your life.
- Isolation and alienation. Being a mother in our Western culture can be a lonely experience. Whole wads of time with only infants for company does something to a person's brain. Adults without a small person in tow can seem like a different species. It can be a 24/7 job literally just to manage necessities – dressing, bathing, feeding, sleeping and keeping a functional space to do all that in. Being able to communicate the enormity of the task you are undertaking is not top of your priority list.

I feel the roots of the problems in our culture are found in this programming we receive in our early years. ***A mother in the West is likely to feel that it's not OK to admit that she is struggling, and to ask for help. She is likely to feel that mothering is hard and not a task that is supported within the wider culture.*** She passes all this programming onto her children. While she is pregnant and breastfeeding, she is passing this trauma onto her children. We grow up with the imprint of this struggle. How different would our culture be, if our first seven years were a time of relative abundance and prosperity. If we were imprinting our children with the reality that life will support them, that their needs will be met, that it's OK to ask for help, that life will flow with them, not hold them back.

I always say, find out what a person's relationship is with their parents and you can see how they treat other people. We are all a bunch of seven year olds walking round dressed up as adults. If we had got the attention we needed as seven year olds then there wouldn't be so many problems in life. When we give mothers support they need, they can support their kids better. It's not even about money (although that plays a part), it's about respect and validation. It's about giving them support and appreciation. It's about making sure their voices are still heard. I think that was the hardest thing for me, feeling like I had no voice. Feeling like I had so much to say, but no way to get it out there because I was drowning in responsibilities. The effort it takes to just get everything done leaves nothing left for the things we want to do.

I had no choice really but to accept that I was less important than my kids, and as they were the main people in my life, I internalised that belief and took it out into the world. I then attracted situations where I was treated as unimportant. Although I knew in my heart that I was! I expected the world to treat me otherwise. I was programmed for injustice, if you like. It's very hard to shake that off.

The financial limitation placed on a woman while she is raising children is perhaps the main way we oppress her and do our children a disservice. A mother should not have to worry about how she will pay the rent and where the food is coming from, that at least should be a given. And yet few are the mothers who can meet their basic needs by themselves when their children are small. I was so torn – I wanted to be there for my kids, to be an emotional rock for them, but the stress of doing everything it takes to run a household single-handed was crippling. If you are one of those fortunate enough to be able to raise children without financial insecurity, I hope you realise what an incredible blessing and privilege that is.

122

It all comes back to capitalism, and prioritising profit over people. When our culture places making money as the highest activity, women suffer. We need to question our need for continuous consumption. If our needs shift to more simple people-centred ones, the more vulnerable members of our society would get adequate care, rather than being trampled on in the fight to have, do and say more. If a greater portion of our taxes went into supporting families with small children over say, weapons, or bailing out bankers, we would all benefit.

I guess men fetishize the young woman because she has needs they can understand - she is looking for a man to give her a baby. But the complex demands of a mother and the challenge implicit in an older woman who is no longer fertile are more complex to deal with, so it's easier to sideline them rather than address the real issues at stake. But of course, in that lack of engagement, we all lose – men lose out on the depth of experience that an empowered woman can bring to their lives and the world, and the next generation miss out on an integrated childhood that is rooted equally in male and female strength.

When I was younger, I would visit older women's houses, grandmothers of friends or cousins, and who had long ago left home, and wonder why they kept everything so pristine. As the only occupants of the home were usually a lady and her husband, I couldn't understand why they kept everything as neat and polished like a 5-star hotel. I really couldn't see what would motivate anyone to do that. But once I started raising kids myself, I began to see the logic in it. When you have small kids, every day is a battle, and your home is the warzone. Can you get through the day making sure everyone stays happy, gets fed and watered, the house doesn't fall apart, and without losing your sanity? Actually on many days, the answer was no. So as the children grew, and I began to gain some solid ground, I found a new satisfaction in actually managing to maintain order in the home. My zeal for a clean, neat and tidy home had reached new levels, purely because it had been put out of reach for so many years. So I could see how, as their children grow, women start to make the home their primary task.

But more than that, if a woman has been excluded from society and made to feel secondary during those child-rearing years - because of her status as a lesser breadwinner - then this fortifying of the home becomes more about creating a domain over which she has dominion. The less control she has over external events, the more impotent she feels in the world. This can mean a greater need to exert a control over her own home which can easily descend into an authoritarian regime. Everything must be perfectly just so, or there will be trouble. She needs to feel important, and that does not happen when she walks down the street, so she must make doubly sure that it happens at home. A woman who feels at place in the world, does not go to such great lengths to wield or maintain power on a domestic level.

Can you imagine the amount of energy freed up when women realise this? When we stop worrying over our insecurities, and instead worry about confronting the demons who perpetuate them? When we cease restricting our power to the private sphere, and feel confident enough to unleash it on the wider world, there will be revolutionary times indeed.

Summary

- How you parent is a very individual choice, but how you are treated as a parent should not be.
- Mothers are less valued than young, fertile women in our culture, and that damages everyone.
- Giving birth and raising children is when you are giving most, and yet in this selfish world, mothers with their extra demands are treated as an inconvenience and an annoyance.
- All of society would benefit if mothers were given a basic amount of financial and emotional security, so they can devote themselves fully to raising healthy and well-adjusted individuals.
- Being a mother is when a woman is most in her primal power, and if she can't find an outlet for that, the woman can very possibly turn in on herself and focus her energy on being very controlling over her home and family.

Me? No. Pause....

When your life is fueled from your inner Divine Goddess self, the clock literally stops. And life becomes the joyous heaven on Earth adventure that it was designed to be. — **Christiane Northrup, M.D.**

I think what has been happening in perimenopause for women in the West, is that we stop being able to trade in our fertility, which is the only currency men readily give to us. So suddenly, with that source of power removed, we are forced to confront the question, "What is our true value within the culture?" And most women come to the conclusion, not very much. This is what makes us angry. It's not our hormones. It's the long-denied but finally unavoidable fact that what we have to offer is taken thanklessly, if at all. That we have been largely taken for granted throughout life, and there is absolutely no reason why that is going to change now that our only valuable currency (our sexuality) has dwindled. That the only way to change this bitter reality is by doing it ourselves, and actually we're pretty exhausted from all the battles we've already been through. It's only women of extreme gumption, or the ones who have that rare and wonderful thing called support, that are able to face the epiphany of menopause and not be immobilised by it.

I had always known that my life would get going at 42. I just always knew that. And indeed, 2012 was a glorious year, a year where I finally, for the first time, felt that my work was being recognised in the world, and people appreciated me and what I had to offer.

So, at a time when I finally felt I was getting what I wanted out of life, I was surprised to find myself less than ecstatic. I remember feelings of inexplicable discomfort surfacing throughout 2012, but I clearly remember by January 2013, I felt depressed, and I didn't really know why. I am a naturally ecstatic person, I've always been someone who dances for no reason and wants to smile at everyone. But I felt empty, burned out, and disillusioned.

It took the best part of two years to regain my balance: by November 2014 and my 44th birthday, I was feeling like myself again. But during that two-year period, I did a lot of inner exploration as well as outer research to get to the heart of what was going on. I believe joy is our birthright, that moving through daily life in a state of grace and bliss is what we should be experiencing, and that miracles are woven into the fabric of everyday existence. So I wasn't going to accept this state for any longer than I had to, I was going to move beyond it and get back into my sweet spot again.

I realised that the catalyst for what I was going through was menopause, and I started to read all the books on the subject I could get my hands on. But every book presented menopause as a challenge to be surmounted, as an unavoidably stressful and traumatic experience. None of them spoke to my experience. It seemed to me all these authors, as pioneering and ground-breaking as their work is, were missing the basic point here. From my perspective, it seemed like an awfully large elephant in the room. Menopause is **not** primarily about hormone levels and how they adjust at this stage in our lives, that is a natural biological occurrence. *Menopause is about what happens when those hormone levels interact with our perception of reality and the lives we have created based on that perception*. If our perception is out of alignment, and if our lives are out of alignment, that will create the turmoil that so many women experience.

In order to have a smooth transition, we need to have taken care of ourselves and made conscious life choices in our 20s and 30s. If we want to live a vibrant life beyond 60, we need to ensure that our 40s and 50s are not spent trying to reverse the wrong turnings we made when we were younger, but instead building a foundation for future success. Our menopause guru Christine Northrup tells us that *menopause is not solely a result of hormone levels, as conventional wisdom would have us think, "it's the combination of hormone levels with pre-existing brain chemistry along with life*

situation. *"* Or, it's what happens when a shift in hormonal balance collides with an overload of undealt with trauma and built up stress.

All these "menopause cures" are still laying the problems women experience at this age on the doorstep of our biology, rather than our poor lifestyle choices, undealt with trauma and the imbalances in society - particularly in women's roles within society. It's still a fundamentally disempowering stance to take, to say, this is something horrible my body is making me go through, and I will battle it however I can. Rather, the body's infinite wisdom is sending signals to correct our lives so we can live to our potential. The empowering viewpoint is to see our bodies as the intelligent force at work, and realise it's the wider culture that needs to be fundamentally changed to reflect what the wisdom of our cells makes clear to us at this age. We must own up to our decisions and choices, and alert ourselves always to their authenticity and integrity, to ensure our future successes. We are taught to compromise and deny ourselves in order to survive, but that reality is outdated. Compromise and denial leads to suffering, only honesty and openness will allow us to continue to evolve. Any decisions we have made up to that point that limit and restrict us will come up to be examined in this period. If we can't deal with that, it will manifest in a physical condition in the body, such as osteoporosis, or cancer. And if we still can't deal with it then, we will pass over and be given another chance to start again in a new form. But life is about constant evolution and growth, and it does not allow stagnation. If there is any part of you that is stagnating, it has to die.

I feel the most important ways a woman can ensure she has a smooth transitional period in her 40s, is to make sure she makes the right life choices and looks after her health after puberty. If you come through adolescence following the existing pathways of working for the system and existing to please everyone else, you are going to have challenges ahead of you. If you ignore your health and choose to "eat whatever you like", drink regularly, and indulge in recreational drugs, it's going to catch up with you in some way or another in your 40s. I am more than ever grateful for the choices I made in my early 20s. I've been vegan since I was 19, and on a high raw diet since I was 21. Since the age of 30, I've been on an exclusively raw vegan diet. I've done yoga as much as I can fit into a normally hectic schedule since I was 20. I have never worked full-time for anyone else. I have always followed my dreams, and I've always valued friendships over career, and freedom over money. All these choices mean I am now experiencing menopause, a time of increased intuition and sensitivity, as part of a natural unfolding into a new cycle, not a trauma to be fought against (although I did need to learn to slow down.)

I feel more than ever that it's vital to pass this information onto the next generation. The choices you make in your 20s are so crucial. I feel that around the age of 42, it was like my head popped out of a tunnel. Your 20s and 30s are a time for working your ass off. You can handle the stress. I worked so hard and did so much, particularly in my 30s, but no-one told me about this invisible finish line I was going to hit. There is a point in your early 40s when your body just says no! It's time to stop, slow down and look at the view. If you like where you've got to, and you're happy with the view, then there's no problem. But if you don't like your view, you've got a massive issue on your hands, because now is not the time to be moving seats. The seatbelt sign is on and if you move around you're going to experience turbulence!

My personal conflict came because I didn't realise it was time to slow down and instead continued to try and slave drive myself into being as busy and relentlessly productive as I had been in my 30s. But my heart wasn't in it, so it was leading to increased stress and depression. Once I adjusted my sights, and learnt to work with my new rhythms, I have actually found myself even more focused and creative than previously. I cut a lot out of my life that I no longer needed, and I said no to a lot of things that I had always really wanted to say no to. I felt that I couldn't play small anymore, I just literally couldn't. In uncomfortable situations before I would've just shrunk down to accommodate them, and then had to spend time afterwards expanding again. Now I couldn't shrink down, it meant I had to extricate from the situation fast, and make sure I really learned how to stop attracting those situations into my life.

No-one warned me I was going to reach the finish line, and I think it was the shock of it which took some adjusting to. Being so fit and healthy and youthful, I presumed I could carry on at the same back-breaking rate forever. My 40th birthday seemed like a bit of a joke – (I hired out a rink, got some of my friends to DJ, fed everyone raw chocolate, and had a Roller Disco for over 100 people). I didn't expect anything to change. But by 43, I really started feeling like a different person. My eldest son was 16, and I felt the process he was going through in adolescence seemed very parallel. Adolescence is an intense growth period, during which change is accelerated. The difference between a 14 year old and a 16 year old is massive, and again the difference between a 16 year old and an 18 year old is almost unrecognisable. I could see how they might not be able to recognise themselves, and actually the most important thing during this period is that they just relax and take time to get to know themselves. As the hormone balance is so fragile, it's important that they get enough sleep and don't encounter too much stress, in order to stay balanced and healthy. I felt the same need to slow down and put myself first. All through my 20s and 30s, I had been last on my list. Getting everything done for everyone else and being busy in the world, was most important. Now, I started to feel more particular in my requirements. My ability to tolerate uncomfortable situations diminished massively. No more sleeping on sofas when I travelled, or standing in long cold nightclub queues. I needed to be treated properly and treated well. For the first time in my life, comfort was my priority, and minimising stress was a necessity.

I think, had I known that my energy levels would dip at that age, it would have been a lot easier to manage. But instead, there was a whole year, when I kept pressing on, trying to make myself fit into a coat that was now too small. In the same way I think we manage adolescence really poorly as a culture, I think we manage this transitional phase appallingly. I am really grateful that I have got to a place in my life where I can stop. I have achieved financial independence, my children are at an age where they don't need me so much, I am doing work that I love and I have a brilliant social life. It's ok to stop and smell the roses, and I'm really enjoying that. But I can see how, if I didn't have one of those elements of the puzzle in place, it would be a very different story. My ability to deal with discomfort is so massively diminished, I can see how, if I was a person who wasn't happy in her work, who was financially insecure, whose children were still young, or who hadn't cultivated a group of friends with whom they felt stimulated and inspired, I would feel at the best irritated, at the worst angry about where I was at.

I think this approximately seven year perimenopausal period is an opportunity for us to deal with anything that we have been repressing up until now in life. If there is anyway in which our lives are not in alignment, it's going to come up now to be sorted out. If we can sort it, we will emerge into our 50s in a very different landscape. We will be ready for a whole new era in our lives, with a different set of priorities and emphasis. If we can't get to a place of balance, then rather than our 50s and 60s being a second age, it becomes a time of declining health, both emotionally and physically. It's virtually guaranteed that we will get heart disease, or diabetes, or cancer, or osteoporosis, or another life-challenging issue.

I believe physical health is important, of course, but more importantly for a woman at this age, it's her emotional landscape that is central to her health. She must make sure that she is being valued at every level – that she is valuing and respecting herself, and that her family, friends and co-workers also value her. If she does not feel fully appreciated and recognised in any one of those areas, I would say it is certain that it will manifest as a physical disorder in order so that she take time out for it be healed.

Menopause Reframed

Just the word menopause is enough to make us shudder. There is nothing cool, sexy, hip or remotely attractive about menopause. According to the literature, we will become evil old hags. We will lose our sex drive, not that that matters, because we will become so irritable and unreasonable, no one would go near us anyway. Life is over, because without our fertility, what use are we? We might as well shrivel up and die of osteoporosis or breast cancer, or one of the other myriad of diseases we will be unable to fend off. Hmmmm.

Long ago, I detected something fishy in our culture's attitude to women. As a teenager, I remember making a collage composed of images of women that I found, contrasted with the headlines written about them. I was shocked at how the imagery I was being exposed to promoted an overtly sexual view of women, implicitly implying to my young impressionable mind that presenting myself as an object for consumption was the way to get noticed in the world. And at the same time, the articles written about women in these same newspapers and magazines depicted us as victims of this same sexuality, likely to be bullied, raped or worse, murdered, for the simple crime of our sex. This sent out an opposing message to me, that actually behaving in the way they seemed to be encouraging on the one hand, was wrong and punishable. I was confused: how was I supposed to act as a woman? There didn't seem to be a way that I could be strong and confident within this model of overt sexualisation on the one hand and strict repression on the other. I don't think I would have called myself a feminist at that age, but I had a strong sense of the injustices that were perpetrated against women and the hypocritical attitudes of the media.

In my 20s at university, I devoured books by writers like Betty Friedan, Kate Millett, and Germaine Greer. I understood more about how women's role in our society had radically shifted during my mother's lifetime, and I had more context, both for the opportunities I did have, as well as those I didn't. I saw both how far we had come, and how far we still had to go.

Then as a mother, my perspective once again tilted dramatically. I read Rachel Cusk and Naomi Wolf. I resented the way, no longer willing or able to trade on my sexuality, I became a second class citizen. Pushing a buggy down the street, I was invisible, I no longer existed to younger women or just about any man. At a time when I was giving, contributing, damn it, literally building our society's future with my own blood sweat and tears, I felt society was affording me the least worth it had ever done. If I wasn't sexy, I didn't have a proper job, and I wasn't making money, then I was inferior in just about every way that the culture deemed important.

When I finished breastfeeding, I made a piece of art called Kiss My Ass. I took loads of pictures of my butt and collaged them. It was a statement about how to get attention, how to get recognised. How I felt that all the wisdom and experience I had gained in that intense period of child-rearing were not deemed in any way useful. What was given emphasis was - 'had I got my figure back, and would I start doing some real work now and stop being a drain on society?'.

This same empty, almost ashamed feeling filled me often as the children got older. When I had whole days without them, I would start to wonder who I was, and what I should be doing. Luckily for me, it was only fleeting, but I always wondered how much more intense it would be for someone without such a defined sense of self as I have. If I, who actually had so much going for me, felt like this - how did other women deal with being what they call "empty nester" syndrome? If you've been out of the workplace for a decade, what's on offer apart from being a dinner lady or working on the checkout? Most of the time, not very much. One friend who I won't name, but who is incredibly successful, talked repeatedly about finding a job waiting tables! To me (and to you, if I named her), it sounded ludicrous, but in her head, the opportunities available to her in her 40s were so limited, she was seriously considering a minimum wage job.

"I used to turn heads, I don't so much anymore. In certain communities I am snubbed – I am beginning to see that ageism is an issue." **Daniela**

During my perimenopausal years, I watched myself turning into a different person again. My wants, needs and desires radically shifted. I became much more concerned with comfort, ease, and avoiding stress, rather than always being ready to leap into battle like I was when I was younger. I didn't feel the need to prove who I am, more to simply enjoy being who I am. I feel this seven-to-10-year perimenopausal period is about taking a step back to experience inward growth, rather than the outward growth that was all-important in my 20s and 30s. I felt I had a lot in common with my teenagers: a shared desire to sleep in all morning, for one (this from someone who until recently prided herself on never getting more than six hours sleep a night and who very often got by on four or five)!

It's really important to schedule lots of me-time, to get a lot of rest, to be able to focus on yourself more than other people during this period. For women who have built a life that revolves around satisfying everyone else's needs over their own, it can be very challenging to reclaim this space, and persuade the people around them that they can do without them. Women tend to become emotional batteries for the men in their lives, and that can work when she has plenty of reserves, but it rarely works during menopause, when she needs to become her own emotional battery. Most men don't like having their power source disconnected in this way and will fight it!

The child, the adolescent, the young single woman, the breastfeeding mother, the empty-nester, they have all departed. During these phases in my life, I occupied very different roles, and took on very different personalities in order to accommodate these roles. Now I feel like I am none of those people, and I am all of them. *I'm not experiencing a decline into old age, I'm experiencing a ripening into a second age.* It's an immensely powerful thing, to be a woman who has child-rearing out of the way, who is financially independent, who knows herself, and is strong and confident in her body. Once again, I will not let the stereotype define me.

Maybe, in all fairness, the taboo around menopause is so strong because until just a few generations ago, there was very little life for women after child-rearing. This sense of a second age, of another fifty years or more of good health and active life beyond the menopause is something few people anticipated until recently. However you handle it, I recommend you subvert the stereotype once again, and make this period of your life powerful, radical and magical.

I think the real crux of it is to see it as a beginning, not an ending. The temptation is to fall into the societal viewpoint and grieve for all we are losing. Yes, there are losses, there is an ending, but what we gain and the terrain we are entering are far more exciting and fulfilling. An empowered woman is a scary thing. She confronts the repressed feminine within us all, and asks us to look at what we are not doing for ourselves, the ways we neglect ourselves. For those who have designed a whole life around denying their goddess energy, a real life goddess is not something they can easily allow. She appears almost unicorn-like, a rare and exquisite creature somehow not of this world. To acknowledge her is to acknowledge a whole part of ourselves that may have been shut down. No wonder this viewpoint isn't part of our common cultural currency. To admit that women age and grow and have even more to offer, demands an entire shift in our worldview. To accommodate this power, we need to rearrange society from the very foundations, to adjust our sails and take a new course.

The Hormonal Process that Occurs

There are three hormones that between them create the menopause: oestrogen, progesterone, and testosterone. Oestrogen is produced by both the ovaries and the adrenal glands. As the amount of oestrogen that the ovaries produce drops, the adrenal glands must take over. If a woman is living a lifestyle where she is already pushing her adrenals to their limit, this is going to be challenging for her. And she will find during this period, that any kind of stress is hard for her to cope with, because she doesn't have the same adrenal reserves she did when she was younger. Kidney support techniques can be very helpful during this period (see Chapter Ten). The amount of oestrogen that's being produced dips around a year before the woman's final period, so during this year, she needs to take it easy and not take on any stressful roles if at all possible.

Progesterone dips much earlier on in the process, and this leads to what is known as "oestrogen dominance". A woman can have low oestrogen, and still have oestrogen dominance, if her progesterone is even lower! Contrary to popular opinion, oestrogen dominance does not mean high oestrogen, but is more likely to mean low progesterone, hence the popularity of progesterone supplements and creams. Obviously, if a woman is experiencing severe symptoms, some kind of progesterone supplementation can be the necessary step to restoring her health and sanity. But I would much prefer to see women trying to allow these rhythms to fall into balance naturally. The two exist in a delicate interplay throughout each month, and interfering with either is not going to allow that see-saw to move up and down gently. Progesterone, like oestrogen, is produced both in the ovaries and the adrenals, doubling the importance of not allowing oneself to risk adrenal burnout. Herbs like maca and black cohosh modulate oestrogen, and help the see-saw balance itself out. I found black cohosh to be the singular most effective herb for me – sadly, it is virtually illegal in the EU currently, under the THMPD regulations.

Testosterone declines with age, but women still make testosterone after the menopause. It is believed that this is one of the factors that makes older women more assertive and self-assured!

"Looks fade and the body changes, that was a big one as I always considered myself very sexy and attractive to the opposite sex. Men would always look at me with great interest . It was hard (and still is) when that stopped. I had to dig deeper and still am in this process of finding that which never changes." **Roisin**

As we've mentioned before, oestrogen and progesterone work in a see-saw action, you can't separate one out from the other, which is why treating women with hormonal imbalances is so complicated. The other thing to remember is that oestrogen affects serotonin production, so not only is a woman a lot less able to handle stress during this period (as her adrenals must take over making oestrogen and progesterone), but she is more likely to have low serotonin and feel more depressed. This joint lack of physical and emotional energy shifts her perspective, and rather than feel able to confront her problems, they can seem overwhelming. Virtually every woman I know, around this age, felt the need to slow down and take a step back, because of these issues, but has done so with a measure of guilt and/or fear. I would love to see this period recognised not as some disease, but as a well-earned vacation! So we can deal with our hormonal shifts and come out the other end renewed and reinvigorated.

Post-Menopause

When my periods stopped, it was very weird, like getting pregnant in reverse. You may well know that feeling when you are trying for a baby, and every day, you pray your period doesn't come, and every day that it doesn't come you wonder if it's too soon to tell people. I wanted to tell everyone I had finished my menopause! When you're pregnant, you can tell whoever you want, even strangers in shops will be happy and excited for you. I felt it was an equally pivotal and transformative moment in my personal narrative, but I barely knew anyone who might be as excited at the news as I was, unless I took the time to painstakingly explain why it was such a big deal.

The last few months, I could tell it was tapering off. Like the day your period comes, and everything around you seems to soften and relax again. Or when you give birth, and the hormonal shift is tangible overnight – for example, while I was pregnant, I remember everything tasted different and smelled different. I couldn't open the vegetable drawers of the fridge because they smelt so disgusting to me, it made me feel nauseous. But literally, the day I had the baby, the smell completely disappeared, like it had never been there. As soon as I missed my first period, almost to the day it didn't come, I felt like my old self again. A cloud lifted, and I again became that person who gets easily distracted into having discos all over the house when she should be working, and stays up all night writing books because she doesn't need much sleep.

But even more than the return to being Miss Always Happy, Always Energetic, the main thing I wanted to celebrate was NO MORE PERIODS! Why aren't women having parties to celebrate this momentous occasion, like we have baby showers and hen dos? It's the best thing ever. No more messy knickers or ruined jeans. No more spending money on taxed (let's not even go there) sanitary products. No more ups and downs – now I am on a steady roll where I don't need to second guess either my optimism or depression and wonder if I should just put it down to the time of the month. No more fear of unwanted pregnancy. No more contraception, that's a big one. I can be with a man, without having an underlying subconscious narrative perpetually running about how risky our intimacy is and whether I want to have his baby or not.

These are all things that pretty much low-level ruin women's lives for a good thirty years, and they are ALL OVER, and I am so, so, so grateful I want to shout it from the rooftops. I wonder once more why menopause is painted so pessimistically, when in fact it's one of the best things that has yet happened to me. I wonder how twisted our stories are, all our stories, when menopause is seen as a disease, when to me it felt more like a cure. When we are not permitted to celebrate the liberation of this milestone, for fear that all the women still imprisoned by their biology will rise up and realise how duped we have been. If older women were given more prominence in our culture, it would shift the entire value of our sex onto our inner wisdom, and the power in a woman's intuition, and away from our primary value being as mere objects to be fertilised.

Summary

- Menopause only sucks if you do
- You need to go into your 40s with reserves or you will hit a wall. Save some of your energy. It's a marathon, not a sprint. You will need to adjust your sails in your 40s, so don't think you can go on at that headlong pace until you drop or you will run into a storm.
- Your perception of your value could drop dramatically, be ready with strategies for boosting your self-esteem
- Don't run on adrenal stress or it will lead to chronic health issues, as your adrenals will impact on your overall hormonal balance.
- Get your eight hours plus to stay youthful. You will need more rest during this period. You will need a lot of inward time.
- Be prepared to become a whole new level of awesome. Menopause is an ending, but this is necessary to pave for the greater things to come. Don't get too caught up in the grieving for what's past, and instead focus on preparing yourself for the beauty ahead.
- Think of this period as a savasana between two tricky yoga poses. Your 20s and 30s was one pose. If you get a good savasana, you will have even more to give to the next pose. If you fiddle with your mat and your hair and your yoga pants, you won't be as ready for what's coming next.

The Spiritual Essence of Woman

Spirituality is the missing link in modern life. The sense of disconnection that pervades everything we do is at the heart of our malaise. When we seek to connect with the divine, it gives us a renewed purpose, that drives us forward, and a faith that gives us peace. Developing the connection to one's spiritual being, exploring the realms beyond the physical, this is important work for us all. In this chapter, I explore how an understanding of our spirituality impacts our lives as women, and gives us meaning beyond that which society imbues us with. It's not a paradox to say that the deeper we come into our spirituality, the deeper we come into our humanity: the more aligned we are, the more we can express the full force of our womanhood.

Patriarchy Sucks

Patriarchy sucks because it would have us living a soulless life, devoid of pleasure and meaning. Patriarchy seeks only to do, to own, to rule, to win. It makes slaves of us all, and keeps us diminished, unable to access our full potential.

To destroy the patriarchy, we cannot use its own tools against it. This is hard, because these tools are so inbred in us, we forget how else to be. We cannot seek to act against the patriarchy; we do not want to rule over it or to defeat it, because in doing so we will become it and we will perpetuate it. We must fight it with all the things it lacks. Compassion. Tenderness. Wisdom. Allowing. In a word: love.

We talk about Queens, but what is a Queen? A good Queen? A Queen is someone who takes care of her subjects, and ensures that her kingdom prospers. She is just and fair. And a Goddess, what is she? A Goddess is an abundant font of truth and beauty, she always has plenty to give, space to listen, healing love to pour over wounds.

These are the qualities we must embody if we want to dismantle the patriarchal structures that keep us confined. If we cannot find them in ourselves, that is hardly surprising, because the patriarchy does not nurture them, in fact it actively seeks to repress them, as it senses the danger to itself inherent in their power. But find them we must if we want things to change. If they are not being offered to us in our lives, we must seek out spaces and places where we can nurture these energies in ourselves.

The feminine energy runs through every living thing, but of course it is more dominant in women than men. At this time, every one of us needs to look inside ourselves and learn how to foster more gentleness and kindness, and men are looking to women for guidance on this. We begin with learning how to find it within ourselves: the love that we seek comes from an inner alignment between heart and mind. Finding that alignment brings us back into alignment with the world, and we begin to experience joy and harmony instead of warring and stress.

We change our mindset from one of fighting what we don't love, and focusing instead on seeking what we can love. *When things are not going the way we would like, instead of trying to control, from fear, we step away, we move back into a place of trust, and we allow what we want to come to us. We breathe, do yoga, swim, walk in nature, play with children, be with animals, sing, dance, eat real food, stare at the stars, bathe in the sun, and reconnect with the bliss.* The bliss that patriarchy continually holds out of reach, dangles in front of us, and has us believe is always only a dream, a fantasy. We can find that bliss on a daily basis, and this is in fact the most essential of work, if we wish to put an end to the current madness.

"I know there is a cellular conditioning that places men and women in different roles and categories, but that it is something that I have worked on shifting because of knowing this, but it was done for a collective reason. I didn't feel the personal effects, although knew I was connected to this belief system merely by being a woman and that was my place

and point of power to effect change for women and men in totality. That is how I could shift it for others, by continuing to be the example of what I believed a new way of empowered women and men equally working in partnership would look like. That started by my making them equal and empowered parts within myself first. I knew right away I would not be a homemaker, and wanted my independence and to create something of my own. That took work and time to do. Through my own actions and experiences, I focused on changing generational and deep-seeded belief systems around how men and women function, in order to achieve the financial security I desired." **Tania Marie**

What Is Empowerment?

Empowerment is knowing that everything that happens in your life is ultimately a reflection of your inner state. And change happens through working on the inner and being at peace with the reflected outer. This is not a finite action with an end goal, this is a daily practice that deepens and becomes more profound over time.

Empowerment is knowing that you are living in alignment – your heart and your mind, your thoughts and your deeds, your body and your spirit, all operate and interact from the same intention, with the same purpose. The meanings we give our lives can be many, but alignment involves a meaning that springs from a deeper place of wisdom than that which occupies the surface of life. It comes from that unseen place, and it has its own logic, a logic we do not need to understand, but we learn it is easier to obey and to trust than to doubt and to question.

Empowerment is knowing that there is nothing to be scared of and nothing to be worried about because every moment of life is a gift and a blessing. We expect, we welcome, and we treasure the blissful moments, because we know we have earned them, we deserve them. We do not flinch from the struggles and the traumas, because we know they are what make us strong, they are what give us our power, and when we welcome the lows as readily as we welcome the highs, we can recognise them as the wonderful gifts that they are.

This is empowerment. Standing strong in oneself. Accepting of it all. Ready to embrace the full rainbow spectrum of our days.

A disempowered life hovers always in the grey areas, never tasting the fullness of life, constricted, frustrated, and blaming others for their situation. A disempowered life disconnects, and separates the different parts of itself as a survival mechanism to get through the day: I will be this person at work, and this person with my girlfriend, and this person with my friends, because to allow one of those aspects of their lives to see the fullness of who they are would disintegrate the whole charade, and that's something they can't risk happening. A disempowered life is always scared of what's around the corner because their foundation is unstable, they know it doesn't take much to topple it. **A disempowered life is dependent on others to perpetuate their sense of self, because they are not drawing from source, and so a disempowered life is always insecure and vulnerable.**

Knowledge of self is the most important gift we can give ourselves. Take time out from chasing around like a headless chicken, as the world would have us do and dive into the waters of your consciousness. Know you cannot drown no matter how deep you go. Empowerment is freedom, true freedom, and freedom is a scarce and precious commodity these days. It's gold: the more you have of it, the richer you are, and it's a wealth far more rewarding and substantial than anything the material world can ever offer.

Just being a woman is a really important part of my work. Not earning money, or achieving status, but simply truly understanding and getting to the heart of, what it means to be a woman in the early 21st century. Every day I seek to show up, to be present, and to express myself creatively, but that's rarely as simple as it might appear. All through my life, I've hit walls, glass ceilings if you like – some created by my own internal self-doubting belief systems, but many more put there by the world. Time and time again throughout my life, I've been shocked at just how off-balance and unfair our society is. It's been hard at times not to let that depress me and hold me back. But I really have seen it as my work to not shy away from that: to face the barriers head on, and keep being true to my female experience while still trying to make my mark in the world. To create a different scenario for myself and so carve that out for all women. A scenario that does not involve looking pretty and keeping quiet as the main predicators for acceptance. A scenario that instead revolves around being heard, being valued, being respected, and being understood.

I think a lot of women do too much. Based on this internalised sense of inadequacy, my personal experience is that many women who are considered successful in this world, are just very good at running away from themselves. *As women, our primary role is to be. To hold space, to hold an energy, to hold a vibration, and to heal the world with our love and compassion.* Candace Pert said it best when she said, "Our cells aren't just in our body, they are a vibration joining all of us." When women's vibration is not at peace and in harmony, then that affects the whole of humanity. But to be successful in our patriarchal culture, the vast majority of women have to take on the qualities of the patriarchy.

To get back into the essence of my womanhood, when life is making too much of a boss of me, I always take a step back. I retreat into my home. I slow down. I sleep, do yoga, hydrate, eat good food, listen to music. I find myself. Once I've found my inner balance, I feel happy again, and then I am moving forwards from a place of internal joy, which will create more joy in my life. If I'm moving forward from any other place, I won't create joyful situations, I'll create more stressful and unsatisfactory situations.

So many outwardly successful women have lost their footing. They haven't carved out time for themselves, so they can't trust themselves. This lack of trust filters through all their relationships, male and female, and it tears at the fabric of our society. We should be talking, we should be looking out for each other, we should be creating a solid foundation for the affairs of

144

the world. Without that foundation, we are weak – we are weak as a sex, and we are weak as a culture. We have been taught that staying at home makes us weak, but actually in getting out of the home, we have gone too far the other way, and done ourselves a disservice, by disconnecting from our primary power.

Our evolution comes from claiming our womanhood, not denying it. It comes from having our affairs in such impeccable order that we also have time for conquering the world. It comes from knowing ourselves, and knowing our people are taken care of. ***When a woman prioritises her career over her relationships, money over her children, external beauty over inner peace, her light goes out, and the light of the world dims a little.***

Please don't get me wrong, I do believe ultimately, we can have it all. But in that is a juggling act of such military precision, and if we are not careful, we drop the balls that are the most valuable, and are left holding the shiny but actually fake ones.

On Meditation

As a young girl, I went to one of the "best" girls' schools in the country. What that meant, in effect, was that I was trained in a highly masculine way of thinking. It was a results-based, ladder-climbing, extremely cerebral upbringing. There was really no option for the feminine in our worldview. No training given in coupledom, mothering, or that other invisible skill, womanhood.

So parenting came as a huge shock. Unless your stated aim is simply not having a nervous breakdown, there's not a lot of visible results that come out of a day looking after small kids. In the adult world, I can whizz through to-do lists like nobody's business. Mummy world, on the other hand, involves a never-ending series of repetitive tasks which it would be foolish to try and "tick off." Laundry done? Someone's just been sick, here's another batch. Kitchen cleared after lunch? But now it's dinner time. Homework checked? Someone else needs chauffeuring to an art lesson. For a long time I found it hard not to resent this endless encroachment on the cerebral. That fast-paced, thrusting, push ahead at all costs thinking was where I felt comfortable. I wanted to race through allotted tasks, not spend an hour discussing Lego men.

But lately, I've got to thinking. As I stand at the sink, washing up teaspoons again (always so many teaspoons, where do they come from, and cups and glasses that are dirty although no-one claims ownership of them). Thinking about how much time motherhood allows for thinking. When we are alone all day, with just the kids and the laundry and the dishes for company, that allows us so much time to ponder on life. To consider and process and expand. All the time I was resenting the endless mounds of encrusted cups and spoons, they were actually giving me one of the greatest gifts in life. The gift of meditation. Of getting clear this relationship to self. If I was getting everything done, like I had believed was so important, I wouldn't have been able to expand in this way. I might have more to show for life materially (heaven knows, a new sofa would be nice!), but I wouldn't be the kind of woman I am.

There is a whole art to being a woman, which is barely discussed, and absolutely not taught in schools. What I have learnt is that people might judge you for what you do – they may be impressed or they may be scornful – but actually, in their summation of you, what matters more, both to them, and more importantly to yourself, is who you are. How much of a man or a woman are you?

Being a woman is a mindset, and one that it is hard to cultivate when society encourages us to think that being a successful woman means thinking like a man. Hard to cultivate when our role models, the most successful women in our culture, sexualise themselves to a degree that is threatening and demeaning to other women. It's great that we can be high-achieving and admired. But we should be able to do it on our terms, not on men's terms. We need to do it by shifting current cultural values, not adapting to them.

So what is womanhood? That's the million dollar question on which this entire thesis hangs. Without that understanding, we are still left floundering, lost in a world which is not our own. I would say, being a woman is not something you do. It's more about holding a space. Think of your favourite auntie or teacher when you were a kid. There was a warmth about her. You felt comforted by her presence. She always had a smile and a cuddle for you, and you never felt judged by her. In other words, being a woman is about coming from your heart. About caring.

This isn't always easy in our modern world. A world that all too often seems over-flowing with anger, pain, hurt and suffering. A world that encourages us to do, do, do, and barely leaves space for being. How can we heal all that? Well, we begin by healing ourselves. Maybe you've tried flower essences, Reiki, EFT, acupuncture, raw foods, superfoods, yoga... the list of healing modalities is endless, but in my experience they are all extremely effective for bringing me back into a place of balance and alignment. A place where I can rest happy in my position in the universe, with faith that everything is as it should be, and there is always time to laugh and play.

Then we can become Magical Women. Not just for our kids, but for ourselves, our friends, all of humanity. All that space we experience: it doesn't have to be framed as a sense of unfulfilment, constant disempowerment, lack of opportunities, and financial disadvantages - we can transform that. We can choose not to recognise it as a negative, but we can choose to explore the potentiality within that. What has all this inequality forced us to become? Personally, being isolated at home for so much of the time made me feel unimportant to the outside world, but that space for reflection also made me calmer, more compassionate, less quick to judge, more ready to forgive. How can that be a bad thing? Because of my academic upbringing, I thought that to be successful I had to have a big house and a bigger bank balance. How wrong I was. To be successful, as a woman, means letting go of all of that. It means surrendering to a greater power than my controlling mind. It means loving, and loving, and loving some more. That might mean myself, or my kids, or my enemies, but loving is what I'm here to do, and loving is what makes me magic.

At university, I was very influenced by Virginia Woolfe. Her seminal text, if you're not familiar, puts forward the idea that a woman needs undisturbed time in order to further herself, the proverbial room of one's own. Although this sounds like stating the obvious nearly 100 years on, back then it was a revolutionary concept to suggest that a woman even had her own interior intellectual life, let alone that there was any value in her developing that.

Recently, I was on a beach somewhere, I think it was Florida. I love spending time on my own, I am infinitely happy in my own company, in fact I often prefer to move solo, unimpeded by the need to consider anyone else's wants and needs. I was on my own on the beach, and I noticed how many other solitary women there were, contentedly reading books or just sunning themselves. It made me think of Virginia and her emphasis on women being allowed to be alone.

A lot of my girlfriends are single where they would rather not be, and although that might seem like a hard and lonely thing, especially given our biochemical need for physical contact and interaction that we have already explored, I had an epiphany on the beach that day. ***Our generation is undoubtedly the first to experience such giant swathes of alone time, time where a woman's needs are not subservient to the needs of her partner or her children. It's such an incredible privilege, and I think it really helps to recognise it as such.*** This is the time that allows us to explore our sense of self and our spiritual essence, it enables us to dig deep and find something greater inside than what society defines us as. It enables us to throw off the limitations of what we are told a woman can be, and find something so much more magnificent.

For your own health, listen to Virginia's exhortations. Seek out that room, be it on the beach, the park, or a hotel. Know that your time in there is valuable not just to you, but to all women who seek to carve out new territories in their lives.

What do you call a housewife who doesn't have a husband?

As a single mum, I often wondered, how is it that this role I undertake can only be defined in relationship to a man, and without a significant man in my life I lack the vocabulary to define the most essential part of my daily existence?

I changed my name to Kate Magic in 2007, yet it took years for people stop referring to me as Kate Wood. Having books published under the name Kate Wood was, I recognise, hopelessly obfuscating, but there was little I could do about that. But again, I wonder, how is it that it is okay for a man to give me a name (Kate Wood was my married name and I was only actually married for seven years), but it is not acceptable for me to give myself a name? That my endowed patriarchal name has more validity than the name I personally feel resonates most strongly with my own self?

When we talk about patriarchy it has connotations of blame, of resentment towards men. But what I think we are talking about here is an idea that is repeatedly coming to me at the moment, and that is the differentiation between the defined and the undefined self. When we undertake any spiritual practice, we are seeking to find the undefined self. The place of no ego, of spiritual flow, where we feel at one with the universe and at peace with ourselves. The trouble is with so many spiritual practices, is that people start using the practice as a way to define the self - as a raw fooder, or a yoga practitioner, or a meditator or whatever it may be. If the practice becomes who you are, you are missing the point of the practice. Practice is just that: it's a daily state of awareness and whatever takes us there is a tool but it is not the practice itself, the practice is in our creation of reality in every given moment.

We live in a culture that values the defined self above all else, and barely gives space for recognition of the undefined self, let alone the development of it. That is what I understand patriarchy as: the need to label, define, own, limit, and put in a box, which in itself has a place and a relevance, but not as the overarching purpose of our lives.

Thank heavens we are moving into a new age, an age where creative freedom will take precedence over formulaic conformity, and an age where, maybe, just maybe, we will have a word for the contribution of a woman who can build a home that doesn't revolve around a man.

By the way, I discovered, many years after I first pondered the question, the name for an unpartnered housewife – it's a housewitch, of course! I wish I had known this at the time, it would have given me strength and power to rename myself in this way, and reframed myself as being at the centre of my world, rather than being side-lined by an ostentatious vacuum.

Summary

- Your spirituality is your indefinable unquantifiable essence.
- You have to carve out time to connect with it or society will rob you of that birthright.
- Your spirituality is all about who you are, the energy you embody. What vibration do you hold. What energy do you give out? Be someone who holds space, who gives off good vibes. What you do is less important than who you are.
- We need more spirituality in this world. Don't be afraid to prioritise it in your life.
- The spiritual life is its own reward. Greater than material rewards, is the sense of working in harmony with the universe, and the way the universe looks out for you when you're looking out for it.
- Abundance flows on the spiritual path with far more ease and grace than it does on the material path.

Lifestyle Tips

The more we surrender into our femininity and flow, the more simple and easy it becomes to fill our days. As you grow into your goddess energy, you will begin to attract everything you need to you. Remember, it's not in women's nature to chase. It might feel good because that's how you've been programmed, but it goes against our nature and causes stress on a deeper level. Cultivate your goddess energy and watch the universe respond. The universe adores a goddess! Before long, it will serve you just the way you always dreamed.

Know that you are enough as you are. Find ways to feel whole, to remind yourself how beautiful you are. When you believe that you are not good enough just as you are right now, you will keep attracting situations to you that reflect that. When you know that you are perfect in this moment, then you attract in situations of a higher vibration. This isn't to say that life becomes perfect and nothing bad ever happens. But that you can see the perfection in everything no matter how it makes you feel.

To find happiness as an empowered woman, I suggest you build your day round a few simple activities:

- **Sleep**
- **Exercise**
- **Nature & sunshine**
- **Cuddles & physical intimacy**
- **Eating well**
- **Staying hydrated**
- **Mindfulness**
- **Dreaming**
- **Identifying your purpose**
- **Building community**

These might sound obvious, and hopefully are already part of your daily routine one way or another, but I think it really helps to identify them clearly, and purposefully ensure that they are all prioritised in our lives. It's all too easy to let one or two slip and then wonder what the malaise that we are feeling is. I would say all these activities are key for women to achieve hormonal balance – and remember, without hormonal balance, we can't be happy. We may get very good at faking happiness, and we may be very good at masking how we are feeling, but without these elements as our foundation, all the material success the world can offer will still have us feeling a little lost and missing something.

It may seem a lot, to build all these activities into your day. It may well demand a rethink of your life. But I would venture to say that it's not possible to find sustained happiness within the confines of the modern western lifestyle. That once we understand ourselves as empowered women, we will make different choices, take different paths in life. These are not likely to be the ones set out for us as working mothers taking on the world fearlessly, and burning ourselves out in the process. They are likely to be more humble, gentle roles, but ones that find us liberated and fulfilled in ways our mothers and grandmothers have always dreamed of. Identify your purpose, do only work that you love, and give equal weight in your life to family and friends alongside career, and personal me-time alongside community building. Work hard, but don't sacrifice your rest. Pay attention to the troubles of the world, but know that a goddess always remains in her heart, that place of divine perfection, trusting and allowing that everything will be ok. If you can balance all these different poles in your life, then you have achieved the mastery of the empowered woman, and you will glide through your day in a way that appears effortless but actually involves incredible amounts of strength and courage. And then, and only then, is it possible for you to be celebrated on a woman's terms: not as a woman doing well in a man's world, but as a woman carving out her own unique female destiny and trailblazing a path so that future generations of women do not need to grow up disempowered. So that girls have role models, older women that they can look up to who were valued, celebrated and praised for their uncompromising commitment to themselves, not just for what they can do for other people at their own expense; women who are powerful on their own terms, not those prescribed for them by the patriarchy.

Sleep

Sleep problems are so prevalent nowadays, we take them for granted, and forget the days when we actually used to consistently get a good night's sleep.

Considering we spend more time sleeping than any other activity, we know surprisingly little about it. I am not convinced we all need eight hours a night – I think the quality of sleep is more important than the quantity, that a healthy person can get by on much less, and that how much a person needs is partly dependent on genes. What I want to discuss here is how to get the best sleep, no matter what time you go to bed and how long you stay there for!

- Number one has to be, turn your phone off! I have a rule of no electronics in the bedroom. If the phone is in the room, I always have it on airplane mode. The amount of people who sleep with their phone on right by their heads scares me – apparently over 80% of teenagers do. I don't allow myself to turn it on in the morning until I'm properly awake and present – no rolling over bleary-eyed and checking Instagram before you're even out of bed! I try and keep my bedroom as a sacred space, a place of rest, a sanctuary from the hustle and bustle of life.
- Next must be, make your room as dark as possible. I recently had a session in a floatation tank, and when I went to bed that night, I was shocked at how light my room seemed. A float tank is a form of sensory deprivation: in the darkness, floating in a warm Epsom salt solution, the pineal gland can properly activate. I had thought I was going to sleep in a dark room, but having experienced true darkness in the float tank, I realised how far from that I was. Light pollution is a big problem in cities. If your room isn't pitch black when you go to bed, consider blackout blinds or an eye mask (I have a Tachyon mask which I love. Tachyon is a form of quantum healing energy).

- I sleep with an ionizer by my bed. Salt crystal lamps also act as ionizers. Ionizers help remove pollution, and the negative ions mean you will get a more restful sleep.
- Crystals & plants also have a starring role in my bedroom. These will keep you grounded and connected. I have lavender and jasmine, which are relaxing, and aloe, which emits oxygen at night.
- If you are living in the city, I would say a grounding sheet is essential. You can get a small one to go under your feet, a whole fitted sheet, or even a sleeping bag. There are plenty of studies that show how grounding can help with restless sleep and insomnia; if you want to research more, the authority is a man called Clint Ober. Before I had my grounding bag, I thought I slept just fine, but once I had it I realised how I never got that deep sleep that allows us to wake up fully rested.
- I also sleep with my Zapper under my pillow. A zapper is an electrical device which promotes healing and stimulates the immune system. It's fantastic preventative medicine. You can zap in the day time of course, but I do a cycle when I am going to sleep, and if I have time in the morning I do another cycle before I get up.
- If you have any mirrors in your room, you should cover them over. In Feng Shui, mirrors will reflect and bounce energy around the room while you are sleeping, and possibly bring unwanted energies in. For a good peaceful night's sleep, you want to cover your mirrors with a cloth or a sheet (that you can just lift off in the morning, when you want to look and see how few bags you have under your eyes from following all these sleep tips!).
- Finally, do you have a good pillow? Energetically, pillows are absorbing so much of our subconscious energy while we sleep. What else do you spend so much time in contact with on a daily basis? Make sure you are happy with your pillow. I have my own memory foam pillow that I travel with, to help ensure I sleep well when I'm away from home.

Adrenal stress is one of the biggest plagues in our culture today, caused in part by our fast-paced lifestyles, but just as much by all the electromagnetic pollution that disrupts our energy fields and stops us getting proper rest. Now so many of us are health-conscious, we think about our diet and exercise, but not enough of us give thought to getting really good quality sleep. These are just a few simple, inexpensive things you can do that will make a massive difference to your vitality. Sleep is a vital way to rejuvenate and restore when we are feeling out of whack, and actually how hard that's becoming in our world of electric lights, wi-fi and mobile phones.

"No regular sleep because of small children affects my hormones." **Cerise**

Exercise

Humans are made of water, and water needs to move. If water becomes still, it becomes stagnant. The more we move, the happier we are. Keep this in mind as you go through your day. Always take the stairs rather than the elevator if you are able. Walk up the escalator if possible. I try and stand for twelve hours a day; they say sitting is the new smoking! I have a standing desk, so when I am working on the laptop, I am standing. It's a compact, inexpensive gadget, like a laptop stand on legs, that you can balance on top of a normal desk or table. Whereas sitting encourages passivity, as we fall back into ourselves, standing encourages activity. I find I am constantly moving my body around, stretching, or stopping for a little dance. When I'm on the train or the bus, or in a waiting room where possible, I will stand. Twelve hours might feel like too much at first, but start off your day like that, and even if you only get to lunchtime, you'll have done your body a service. You'll be surprised at how quickly you build up stamina to be standing until dinner time, and then even past that into the evening.

I cycle everywhere, I go out dancing once or twice a week, and I do yoga as often as possible. Yoga is so much a part of who I am, I find it really hard to identify who I would be without it, and so be objective about how important it is to me. Yoga, as you probably know, means "union," and yoga brings about just that, a union between the mind and body that it is indispensable in our modern world. A daily physical practice deepens this connection, so bringing us solidity and strength. Meditation is a part of any good yoga practice; a way to quiet the mind and focus on what really matters. In our busy lives, we get caught up with our endless to-do lists, and lose perspective on the bigger picture. Any physical activity that brings us back into the present, is a meditation: it might be running, cycling, dancing, yoga, Pilates, chairobics, or any number of disciplines, but whichever we pick, it's vital to build it into the structure of our daily lives, and make it a priority that we don't shy away from. The longer we involve ourselves with the practice, the clearer a pathway it becomes back into our core energy. Schedule this activity into your weekly routine, and don't be afraid to prioritise it over other things people may try to make more important. Carving out this space and time for yourself is crucial for your happiness and well-being. I am truly of the mindset that our body is a gift given to us to treasure and take care of, and I have a duty and responsibility to keep it in as tip-top condition as I can. Yoga is one of the tools that helps me feel really good in my body, like it is a wonderful place to be. When I am stressed and too much in my head, thinking of the million and one things I have to do, yoga brings me back into my body and into the present moment, it stills all the mind chatter. It makes me feel strong in my body, balanced and elegant. When I was little, I wanted to be a ballet dancer! I had ballerina wallpaper, clock, bedspread, everything, I was obsessed. I believe yoga gives me that grace and poise that I so admired as a child.

"Work causes me stress because I often feel like I don't have a voice. If I suppress this feeling, I get the most horrendous mouth ulcers. However, if I keep up my mindfulness practice and exercise regularly, this helps enormously." **Linda**

Nature

Nature is a powerful healer, and the ultimate goddess. When we spend time with her, we become attuned to our own natural rhythms. We reconnect with the bliss of pure existence. If we live in the city, it's essential that we make time to regularly escape and recharge. Too long in the rat race will turn you into a rat. Find nature and find your essence again. There is an intelligence in plants and animals which speaks to our unconscious selves, and reminds us of our own innate intelligence.

At a class recently, when I was talking about how we must all listen to our own bodies and how unique we all are, a man said that, "There is a universe inside every one of us." I love the succinctness of that idea, and how we can apply it to everything we see. There are universes inside universes inside universes. A universe inside that city, a universe inside that church in that city, a universe inside each person in that church. There's the universe of the animal kingdom, and the universe of each species in the animal kingdom, and the universe of each type of animal within that species, and then the universe of each individual creature.

When we open our eyes the idea of poverty and deprivation seems truly ridiculous. There is so much for us to learn from and be inspired by. So many ways that we can grow from this contact. The joy that this earth can bring, through truly engaging with the vegetation, the animals, and the humans, is an infinite blessing that will never diminish.

Our indoor lifestyles are not natural or healthy. The more time spent outside, the more we will feel connected and at peace. The more time we spend holed up inside, the more we feel discomfort and dissatisfaction. It's such a simple thing, and usually the simplest things are the most overlooked!

"I'm perimenopausal so at times every little thing causes me stress. I find I'm less tolerant of people than before. I find walking helps, also finding a space to go where I can be totally alone for a while to sit in silence." **Lis**

We need air, light, and the electrical connection to the earth to be happy. Fresh air, not city air; sunlight not cloudy days or indoor lifestyles; barefoot on the earth, not shoes on concrete. Find ways to build these habits into your lifestyle, if they are not a part of it already. If you don't live somewhere where the air is good, find ways to get away to places where you can breathe deep. If you work indoors, find ways to take breaks and feel the sunshine on your skin. If you live in the Northern hemisphere, with long periods without sun, invest in daylight bulbs, or visit an Infra-red sauna, so your brain and body can detect the right UV light even in the absence of actual sun. ***If you are not in regular close contact with the earth, consider getting grounding devices. You can buy sheets, mats, or shoes,*** *which contain silver threads that act as a conductor to the earth. The difference in well-being when using one of these devices is immense. The earth is like another brain we can use, another source of energy to tap into,* and most of us living in cities are not even remotely tuned into it. We can't feel happy and whole when we are living in such a state of disconnection from our mother planet!

To get enough Vitamin D, we need 15 minutes of direct sunlight a day, and that's proper sunlight, not through a cloud, and on the full body, not partially clothed. Added to that, in the Northern Hemisphere, we only get the right UV rays from April to September, so it's essential that we consider other ways to get enough sunlight. If you do the maths, 15 minutes a day works out at one 8 hour day a month, and as vitamin D is stored in the body for up to two months, it's perfectly valid to look at it that way. Winter sun holidays are so essential, and so much more accessible now. If it's within your time and money constraints, it's one of the best things you can do for your health over winter. I try and ensure I am going to be somewhere sunny at least one weekend every other month.

Cuddling

Women need physical contact much more than men, because we produce much higher amounts of oxytocin. If you're not fortunate enough to have a human in your life right now for daily cuddles, find other ways to get your oxytocin needs met. The two best ways are: massage – schedule regular massages for yourself, weekly if you have the budget; and pets – we can still get that oxytocin high from cuddling with animals rather than humans. Don't get stuck on cats and dogs either; one of my best friends has a snake, and another used to have rats. Any animal that you bond with and enjoy physical contact with is going to provide an oxytocin hit.

I've been on a raw vegan diet since 1993, and I've made a career out of educating people about raw foods since 2002. Please do check out one of my earlier books on raw foods and explore this wonderful medicine, for that's really what it is. Raw foods just make everything easier, and add superfoods into the mix and really you're talking a whole new level of health and happiness. Truly, a quantum leap. I don't believe fully raw suits most people, but I do believe gradually introducing more raw foods and superfoods into your diet at a pace that feels comfortable is something everyone can benefit from.

Remember, over 90% of our serotonin is produced in the gut, so your diet has a major impact on your happiness levels. Including fermented foods in your diet on a regular basis is one of the key ways to naturally boost serotonin levels. Scientists are only just discovering the gut-brain axis and how it works, but in a rapidly developing field known as gastroneuroenterology, there are clear links being made between how what we eat affects our mood. One of the very best ways to naturally boost your mood with food on a daily basis, is to include fermented foods.

- Fermented vegetables eg, sauerkraut, kimchi
- Fermented drinks eg, kefir, kombucha, jun
- Fermented dairy products eg, unpasteurised yogurts and cheeses
- Fermented macrobiotic products eg, miso, tempeh, natto

These are all best if you can make your own, and the process is much simpler and easier than you might imagine. If you don't have the time to make your own, seek out local brands made by small producers, and always check that they are not pasteurised, as the heat involved in the pasteurisation process will destroy the living organisms that you are looking for.

Avoid refined sugar, non-organic foods, fluoridated water and toothpaste, and antibiotics, as these all destroy the balance of healthy bacteria, whereas the fermented foods promote the growth of these good bacteria. If you have been on a course of antibiotics recently, or been travelling far and exposed to foreign bacteria in the air and water, then it's a really good idea to do a course of high-strength probiotics in order to restore the healthy bacteria. When our guts are out of balance, our minds are out of balance, it's as simple as that; it's impossible to feel the sense of peace and focus we are seeking when our guts are messed up. The other big advantage, if you're figure-conscious, is that regular use of probiotics reduces bloating and gives you that elusive flat tummy.

If depression is an issue for you, as well as including fermented foods, I recommend investigating the following supplements:

- **St John's Wort** – the active ingredient in this herb is Hypericum, and it has been shown to naturally boost serotonin levels. Try it in tincture or capsule form.
- **5-htp** has been shown to be 400% more effective than anti-depressants! 5-htp is the natural precursor to serotonin. It is present in large amounts in the Ayurvedic herb mucuna, which I recommend highly. Just quarter of a teaspoon of mucuna is a good daily maintenance dose. I add it to my hemp or coconut milk, and put it in chocolates.
- **Raw chocolate, or cacao**, is high in tryptophan, which is also a precursor to serotonin. Make your own raw chocolate containing mucuna for a great natural lift.
- **Turmeric** has been shown to be a more effective anti-depressant than Prozac. It's the curcumin in turmeric that makes it powerful – it's a good idea to combine your turmeric with a pinch of black pepper, as the piperine in pepper increases bioavailability of turmeric by 2000% (that's not a misprint). Buy good quality fresh root, organic turmeric powder or turmeric extract, not just curry powder from the supermarket.

Anti-depressants work by blocking the natural uptake of serotonin, so the herbs listed above can work against any pharmaceutical medication. It's not recommended to take both together as this could be unhelpful and make the depression worse. These herbs are highly effective for mild depression; clinical depression is a more serious matter and should be treated by a specialist.

If you're under any kind of physical or emotional stress, either because you're in a difficult situation you can't immediately extricate yourself from, you've got a physical ailment you're dealing with, or you're taking too much on and doing too much, then consider the following adrenal support herbs. The adrenals, remember, sit on top of the kidneys, so in Chinese Medicine, anything that strengthens the kidneys, strengthens the adrenals.

- **Black foods**. In Chinese herbalism, black foods are considered kidney support foods, which is one of the reasons for the recent popularity of black beans. Try also black rice, black sesame and black tahini.
- The adrenal support herbs in Chinese medicine **are Eleuthero, Astragalus, Cordyceps, Rhodiola, and Licorice.** I have used all of them at different times. Eleuthero is particularly good for the kidneys. Astragalus also supports the spleen. Cordyceps is a medicinal mushroom which is good for energy and strength. Rhodiola is mildly stimulating, though not as strong as caffeine. Licorice you are probably familiar with! Chew on licorice sticks to replenish energy, or drink licorice tea. All these herbs are necessary in small amounts only. Buy herbal extracts from a good brand such as Jing Herbs or Dragon Herbs. Take quarter of a teaspoon a day in a hot drink or in a plant milk.
- You might want to look at the **kidney cleanse** protocol at the end of this chapter as a method of de-stressing.
- **Salt baths** are a wonderful way to unwind and relax. Epsom salts and sea salt will remineralise the body and are both very detoxifying. Epsom salts are high in magnesium, which is the main mineral for the heart, and also relaxes the joints. In the bath, the magnesium is absorbed into the skin and so this is a very effective way to get magnesium into the body. Use at least one cup of salt – you can use as much as one kilo at a time! Remember, adrenaline releases magnesium from the cells, so the more stressed you are the more in need of magnesium you will be.

The best supplements for hormonal balance are

- **Maca** which I think should be available for women on the NHS. It's very rare to meet a woman who doesn't get on with maca. Maca is both one of the best foods for adrenal support, and a natural hormone balancer. All of the issues we go through – adolescence, pregnancy, breastfeeding, fertility, menopause, PMS – maca is very effective at alleviating unwanted symptoms. As it is a powerful adaptogenic herb, it must be taken carefully. Start with a teaspoon, and work up. Most people end up on a maintenance dose of one tablespoon a day, although I do meet people who are taking more. If you find your symptoms getting worse, don't worry, that's part of the healing process. Slow down on the dose of maca and the symptoms should pass within a few days. It's quite common for a woman with PMS to find that in the first couple of months of taking maca, her symptoms are worse, but by the third month, they are gone completely. As maca is a thermogenic food, it's also wonderful for hot flushes, as it helps the body temperature stabilise.

- **Shatavari** is the number one Ayurvedic herb for women, it's also an adaptogen. It's a galactagogue, i.e. it promotes the flow of breast milk. The Ayurvedic translates as "She who possesses a hundred husbands." When I say that in class, people laugh, and no-one has yet admitted to wanting a hundred husbands. But it gives you the idea of the kind of energy you get from taking Shatavari, the energy to deal with as many husbands as you might desire. I love it because it's powerful but in a very feminine way, not aggressive, but reassuring.

- In Ayurveda, the three herbs that are most used for women are **the Three Beauties, Shatavari, Ashoka and Bala,** and they are great taken in combination. Ashoka translates as No Grief, and is good for hormonal depression. Bala was apparently the goddess Parvati's favourite herb, the goddess associated with beauty and grace.

- **Royal Jelly** is what the Queen Bee feeds on, and the Queen Bee is twice the size of the worker bees. She lives 45 times longer than them, and she produces up to 2000 eggs a day. A great one for fertility, and generally connecting you with your creative female essence.

Try and avoid the comfort food trap. Comfort food generally means carbs; carbs provide a short-term serotonin release, which is why they are addictive. They also cause spikes in the blood sugar, which can disrupt insulin levels if you become too dependent on them. I follow a ketogenic diet, which means my body is fat-burning. The carb content of my diet is minimal, and instead I get my fuel from fats. When the body adjusts in this way, it becomes very efficient at burning off fats, and so it's easier for the body to maintain its ideal weight. When you are using carbs as fuel, then the body is more likely to store the fats. So with a high carb diet you are going to be more likely to put on weight than with a high fat diet! But more importantly, without the ups and downs of carbs, my mood and energy levels stay much more consistent and equanimous. You want to get your fuel from the healthy fats in avocados, olives, nuts and seeds, coconut and cacao. Minimise rice, wheat and potatoes, and instead go for the alt-carbs: cauliflower rice, flax bread and crackers, courgette pasta.

Carbohydrate addiction is compounded by the fact that cortisol is released when your blood sugar is low, so you get your serotonin high from the carbs, only to feel stressed when the carb high subsides. That stress has you reaching for more carbs! Stick to a low-glycaemic diet as much as you can – I snack on low-sugar raw chocolate (I make it myself with sweeteners such as stevia), seeds, and crackers. I rarely have sugary snacks and hardly eat any fruit. This carbohydrate addiction is one of the main causes of diabetes. As a person's blood sugar is rocking up and down, they develop insulin resistance, which means the body keeps making insulin but it can't get what it needs. So the person keeps eating because they don't feel full. And one of the chief causes of insulin resistance is elevated cortisol! Remember, adrenaline is the kind of stress hormone you produce when you are running for a train, or think that you lost your phone. But cortisol is produced when someone has constant low-level stressors running in the background eg, someone who is doing a stressful low-paid job they don't enjoy. This kind of person has abnormally high cortisol levels, because they are in a situation where they don't get to de-stress enough. So we can see how this is such a common picture and an easy trap to fall into: stress leads to carb-addiction, leads to diabetes. If this sounds like you, two things need to happen immediately – you need to cut the carbs and switch to a low GI ketogenic diet, and you need to look for new ways to de-stress eg, yoga, a woman's group, outdoor exercise. Once you have this under control, then you will feel calmer and more able to see solutions to extricate yourself from the stress that you are under.

Leptin is another important hormone to mention in relation to hunger. Leptin and ghrelin are the two hormones that regulate appetite – leptin is an appetite suppressor, while ghrelin increases appetite. One of the contributing factors to obesity is leptin resistance, which means a person never feels full, so they keep eating. When we eat a diet that is nutritionally dense, we produce leptin much more quickly. There are two ways to feel full – one is the physical, can't fit anymore in my gut way, which most of us are used to. And the other is by eating a nutritionally optimum diet, so that leptin is produced and the body receives the signal that it can stop eating because it has plenty to work with. It's pretty universal that when people adopt a raw and superfoods diet, they are amazed at how quickly they feel full, and how little they need to eat compared to what they are used to. I believe this is due to the increased leptin that is being released. When we eat comfort food e,. a bowl of pasta, or a conventionally baked cookie or cake, we are filling our stomachs, but there is so little nutrition in those foods, the body remains hungry and so we keep eating, searching for the missing nutrients.

Hydration

I personally feel that hydration is the number one most important thing for our cells. Our bodies need to be fully hydrated for our cells to communicate, without enough liquids, all the nutrition in the world isn't going to be enough. I also believe that when we get our nutrition in liquid form, that's the easiest way for the body to absorb the nutrients.

"I get overwhelmed by society, over-stimulated by large crowds. Usually staying hydrated and keeping to myself in a secluded place where I can do some artwork helps a lot." **Jasmine**

The thing that exhausts me most in my life currently is travelling. I spend a lot of time on trains and planes, going round the UK and the world. Not only is it time-consuming, I am usually in cramped, over-crowded conditions, exposing myself to a huge amount of foreign bacteria from the people close by me and the dirty public transport systems. If I've had a long day travelling back from an event of some kind, the next day I can feel low-energy and depleted. I know for myself, the number one thing to do in that situation is make sure I spend the day getting fully hydrated again, and getting some yoga in. If I can get in five litres of liquid – fermented drinks, medicinal teas, coconut water, green juice and plant milks, I know I will be up and running again the next day.

Try and get in the habit of drinking first rather than eating. Often, you will find you were actually just thirsty, not hungry. Aim to drink minimum three litres a day: a litre in the morning, a second in the afternoon, a third in the evening. Avoid drinking plain water as it doesn't hydrate you in the same way. Plain water acts a flushing mechanism in the body: great for getting rid of toxins, but not so good for hydrating. Adding fats and minerals to your drinks is the best way to hydrate, which is why plant milks and green juices satisfy the body so much more than plain water.

- **Fermented Drinks** – these are kefir, kombucha and jun. I make my own and recommend it highly. Having one of these is like having a pet. You need to take care of it, and you can't just go on holiday and leave it! We have already discussed the gut-brain connection; I believe drinking these fermented drinks is the very best way to strengthen this gut-brain connection. You can buy them in the stores now, but often they are too sweet or too vinegary, and they really are so much more nurturing if you can make your own. I don't think it's good to have them in too large amounts though. If I'm really busy I will have up to a litre in a day, as I find them very energising, but I think 500ml a day is a good maintenance amount ie, a glass in the morning and a glass in the evening. It's very good to have first thing in the morning and in the evening a little while after dinner, in order to settle the stomach before bed.
- **Medicinal teas** - I usually drink 1-2 litres tea a day. I use a coffee-press, and I always use the actual herbs rather than tea bags. I use Chinese herbs such as Reishi and Gynostemma, Ayurvedic herbs like Shatavari and Ashwaganda, and European herbs like Raspberry Leaf and Damiana. They are a wonderful way to hydrate and tonify the system.

166

- **Plant milks** – I usually make my milks with hemp or coconut. You can use whole hemp seeds, which you need to strain, or the shelled seeds. To make hot milk, I use a tablespoon of coconut oil. Then I add superfoods such as maca, chaga, Reishi, mucuna, and typically just a little stevia to sweeten. This milks are very nourishing and sustaining, and a great thing to include between meals to curb your appetite.
- **Green juice** – I am a great believer in the power of green juice, but when I say green juice, I do not mean all those fake green juices you find in shops nowadays! Green Juice was created by Anne Wigmore as part of the healing programme at the Hippocrates Health Institute in Florida, and it contains only green vegetables, no fruit. To my mind, putting fruit in a green juice is like putting eggs in a cake and calling it vegan: the point of green juice is that it is all greens and no fruit. I make juice with a base of cucumber, celery, lemon and ginger, and then in go any other greens I have to hand eg broccoli, kale, spinach, parsley. Also, my other tip is not to use a juicer. Juicers are expensive to buy, fiddly to use, and worst of all, time-consuming to clean. I blend all my veggies up in my blender, and then strain it through a milk bag. This way, I can make a litre of juice AND have cleaned up in under 15 minutes.
- **Coconut water** is best mixed with greens. Coconut water is a brilliant blood purifier, and so are wheatgrass and the other green powders, so when you mix them together, not only is it a tasty way to get your green powders in, it also provides you with maximum benefits. Coconut water that comes in cartons is pasteurised so not raw, but that's the one I go for in the UK, as I would have to be a millionaire to drink as much as I do of the fresh stuff!

Positive reframing

"It's stressful being a black single woman, but if we switch the word stressed to blessed, we are half way free of the stress we think we feel. Self-talk, using our words to edify ourselves and carry ourselves through trying times, is a powerful tool." **Jimetta**

First off, the important thing is not to feel bad about your own negativity, that's not the healthy direction to move in. Our culture is constructed to

167

keep us small; it encourages us to think of what we don't have, it reinforces inadequacy, rather than being uplifting and supportive. So it's hard to extract ourselves from those patterns. And as we are constantly creating with our thoughts, the world we are creating reinforces that belief system, and it becomes more and more entrenched.

But never fear, because the mind is actually very easy to train. It's surprisingly simple to replace negative thoughts with positive ones. And as we see the results very quickly, it's very encouraging once we get started.

Pick a time when you know your thoughts always run away with you, and you've got fifteen minutes or so to examine them. Maybe that's first thing in the morning or last thing at night. It might be when you're doing the housework or commuting. If you haven't got fifteen minutes of solitary time in the day, then you need to create that time. However you do it, it needs to be a regular daily habit to be most effective.

As the troubling thoughts cross your mind, hear them clearly. Don't dismiss them or bury them, listen to them. Often part of our trauma comes just from not being heard. Things seem much worse when we can't share them. So make sure you are fully hearing yourself and recognising the pain in what is troubling you. You need to embrace that pain before you can let it go. Sometimes at the beginning that could be all you have time for. If you have been suppressing those thoughts, then allowing them to rise to the surface can be a long part of the process. It's OK to be sad, it doesn't mean we are a failure or even a bad person. It means we are a strong person and a brave person because we are facing up to our demons rather than running from them like we are taught to do. And the brain is very clever: after we have cried a lot, it releases endorphins to rebalance, so we can feel exceptionally happy and peaceful.

Once the pain has passed and we can look at it objectively, the next step is to validate it. Another reason we dwell in negative thoughts is because we feel ashamed or guilty about them. We often need to reassure ourselves that it's ok to feel this way. For instance, if your life is outwardly successful, but you feel deeply resentful about what you had to sacrifice to get there, you may feel it's churlish to express dissatisfaction with what you have. Often I find in my quest to focus on the positive, I am instead burying my negative thoughts, and that makes them darker within my internal landscape. The sooner we can examine a belief and bring it into the light then the less power it has. So whatever you are sad about, acknowledge its existence, and again reassure yourself that you are allowed to have these feelings, they have risen out of the circumstances of your life, and you are not wrong for having them. Again, this could be another long step of the process - feeling comfortable with looking at these aspects of ourselves.

So now we've got them out into the light, we need to transform them. I've written below about how I think many people get the cosmic mirror confused. The important thing to remember about a mirror is that it doesn't reflect things straight at you. It reverses them. So you need to reverse the belief patterns you are running. Identify one of your own negative belief systems, and reverse it to create a replacement mantras.

Here are some examples of the programmes I used to run, and what I said to myself when I heard them start up in my inner monologue.

Programming says: it's hard to make money.

Mantra says: I am a magnet for prosperity and abundance

Programming says: people don't value my work

Mantra says: I recognise the quality of my output and appreciate the authenticity of my work

Programming says: he hasn't called because he doesn't like me

Mantra says: I am a beautiful woman who deserves a man who treats me well

Do you see the connection with all these patterns? As always, it comes back to being the change. The things that we are unhappy about are more often than not situations that we are blaming the world about. Situations where we feel disempowered and discouraged. But when we remember that we are creating reality with our thoughts, then we learn to take it back a step and see how our thought patterns are contributing to our situation. And changing our thoughts is the most sure-fire way to change those outcomes.

For this to be successful, it needs to become a long-term habit. Patterns that are deeply embedded such as the ones around money and love, most likely inherited from our parents, may take decades to fully shift. But as soon as you start doing the work, you will see small, incremental changes that keep you motivated, to keep doing the work and create the abundant life you crave.

It really is magic! When we are on the right track, the universe keeps giving us little signs and rewards to let us know. It's so exhilarating, knowing we have this power. It gives us the strength to keep going, against the odds. The thing is, we may live in a world ruled by fear, but love is the stronger force by far. When we give it a chance to shine, it does so effortlessly, miraculously. When we are sat in the darkness it seems so hard to see what direction to go in, where to look for the answers. But as soon as we light that flame, everything becomes illuminated, our eyes adjust, and we start to perceive the true wonder and beauty of this world.

The Cosmic Mirror is Actually a Hologram

The idea that the world is our mirror, a reflection of ourselves, has common currency nowadays, but I think most people get confused as to what that actually means. I believe that our thoughts are a powerful determinant of our reality – everything we think, believe and do, is a spell, if you like, that we are casting on the world around us, to make it behave the way we believe it should be behaving (for better or for worse). Everything we perceive externally is simply a projected vision of our own internal state. But to my mind, the concept goes much deeper than this, it's more of a hologram than a mirror, so I wanted to expand on it a little.

Firstly, let's get the mirror theory straight. We cannot see the world as it is, because as quantum physics has proved, we change a thing merely by looking at it. Just as the face you see in the mirror is the opposite face from the one everyone else sees (which is why we look different in our camera phone than we do in the mirror), the life you view around you is seen from the opposing direction by everyone else looking at it. Others can see us more clearly than we ourselves ever will; we always have a twisted perspective on our engagement with the world, because we find it impossible to fully take into account the way we alter the situation by being a part of it. We are our own biggest blind spots.

Knowing that whatever anyone says about you, they are really talking about themselves, is the key to accepting both praise and criticism with equanimity. When someone passes judgement on me, for better or for worse, I always keep in mind that they are really telling me something about themselves. If someone tells me I am amazing, I am happy because I have brought out the part of them that is amazing. If someone tells me I am stupid, I am sad, because I have brought out the part of themselves which is stupid. But whichever way it falls, I try not to take it personally. I understand that they are ultimately just seeing a part of themselves that they either do or don't like, in me. I try not to take either the positive or the negative on board, but know they are just projections of the other person's inner state. The only judgement that really matters is the judgement I pass on myself, which is why it's important to cultivate self-love and authenticity. Only I can make myself happy, and I shouldn't give that power away to anyone else.

So, if someone has a positive attitude towards me, I smile and inwardly acknowledge and thank them for their positivity. If someone has a negative attitude towards me, I try and get out of their space as quickly as possible, and just not have any interaction with them. I do not want to perpetuate the negative energies, but when someone has made a negative judgement about you, it is next to impossible not to make a negative judgement back in return. Even if we do it with compassion, such as, "she's only being mean because her mum didn't give her enough attention and validation when she was a child," we are still making an assumption that they are less of a person than they could be, and why would they want to be around someone who thinks that way of them? *We should always seek to spend time with people who lift us up, who admire and respect us, and seek to make us feel good about ourselves. I want to spend time with people and be inspired by them, not make excuses for them.*

If someone acts with hostility towards me, and I am defensive or aggressive in return, I am feeding those hostile energies in themselves and in me. In Masaru Emoto's work, he claims that the most distorted, ugly and chaotic patterns happen in the crystalline structure of water when we ignore it completely. Ignoring is the worst thing we can do because if we are not feeding it with our attention, we are not giving it life, and it will die out. Thus, if we do not like something or someone, to not feed it with any kind of attention, but simply to walk away from the situation, is the quickest and most efficient way to remove that scenario from our lives entirely. Of course, we also need to examine why we attracted that particular scenario in the first place, or we will just attract it in again in another form.

Which brings me to my next point. How do we recognise those patterns in ourselves that come from separation and fear rather than wholeness? And how do we deal with them? What to do about our own projections, the things that we see in others that we don't like? Everything that makes us uncomfortable in other people is really deep down what we find uncomfortable about ourselves. But, this where it gets confusing, because in a mirror remember, everything is inverted. So for example, if someone treats me badly, and I name the quality that I don't like in her behaviour, for example, "She's so arrogant! She genuinely thinks she's better than everyone else"; doesn't that mean that I myself am arrogant, and she is simply reflecting that back to me. Well yes, maybe on one level, she is giving me an opportunity to examine my own arrogant streak. But negative thinking is never helpful, when it is about other people, and especially so when it is about ourselves. If we name the behaviour, but in doing so we are telling ourselves something negative about ourselves, that is not constructive or productive. That doesn't help the other person to grow, nor does it help ourselves. It just makes everyone feel worse. On the other hand, if we don't name the behaviour, that's allowing the other person to get away with behaviour that is not from their heart, and allowing authenticity to go unchecked is not progress either. So how do we progress out of this situation where it seems we can't blame the other or blame ourselves without leading us deeper into negativity?

When we look at our lives through the mirror of ourselves, we have to remember we are seeing everything in reverse. So if someone around you is being arrogant, it isn't a reminder from the universe to curb your own arrogance. It is a reminder from an essentially benevolent universe that you are not arrogant enough, in fact the opposite, you need to be more self-assured! That person is showing you an area of your life in which you are lacking in self-esteem and you have a low self-image. If you had a healthy self-image in that regard, you would have attracted in someone who valued you and didn't treat you badly. So you must learn to love yourself more, raise yourself up in your own eyes, in order to find people who match that self-belief. Any lack we perceive in others is not a message from the universe that we ourselves are lacking; rather it is a reminder from the universe not to perceive lack in ourselves. To love ourselves more and be kinder to ourselves, so we can find that love and kindness all around us is always the mission.

Love is the only currency the universe knows. All lessons are given with love, and when we understand how to receive them with love, rather than fear and self-doubt, we can start passing them with flying rainbow colours.

Dreaming

"Stress can be the pressure that when managed well shapes a woman into the warrior she will need to be to project her own dreams onto this reality." Jimetta

I actually think dreaming could be the most important thing we do. Not to get too whimsical about it, but really, what are we without a dream?

In our modern day lives, we are taught to be creatures of doing. All the emphasis is put on action, and very little on the energy that puts that action into motion. I would say this is because if your motives are impure, you do not want to draw attention to them. If your drive comes from the desire to exploit others for your own benefit, to profit from others' weakness, then you are going to keep that hidden! This is how our current rulers operate: they distract us from noticing by working us harder and harder, so we don't have time to raise our noses from the grindstone. They fill us with propaganda and poisons, to diminish our ability to access the dream state.

If we do manage to free ourselves from those mental shackles, we immediately notice two things. Firstly, how abhorrent the current system is. And secondly, we remember our own dreams, our own desire to create something beyond what is set out for us, to expand into new territories. As the universe would have it, these two things are complementary, and so we can see how our dream will change the system and help make the world a better place.

A dream is nothing without action, but neither is action anything without a dream. We are taught to do, do, do, and maybe save the dream for Sunday afternoons and that one week off a year. We can be the busiest, most productive individuals, but if we don't have a clear drive and intention behind all that business, it will all amount to nothing.

In the past I have had a tendency to overwork, and several times have approached burn out, which has taught me to step back and pay attention to balance. I have come to learn that I accomplish most when I create time for action in my day, and also allow space for dreaming. It's vital that I keep in mind my highest aims and my biggest dreams, or I will end up in dead ends and wrong turnings. Having this space means not being busy all the time, but rather than achieving less, it results in me being more focused with my time and energy, and only devoting myself to tasks and undertakings that are directly related to achieving my end goal. It's been a process of clearing out, and realising how much time I waste on things that are not really important to me. It's a wonderful self-affirming circle: the

174

more effort I put into keeping my intentions clear, the less inclined I am to do anything other than work on manifesting them.

Try it. Set aside a regular daily five minutes minimum (an hour would be wonderful!), to dive deep into your dreams and really feel what they look like. If you could be anything you wanted to be, what would that be? Where would you live? Who would you be spending time with? Immerse yourself in the fantasy, imagine it's real, so you're properly connecting with it on a heart level. They could be big dreams like becoming a professional singer or opening a retreat centre, or it could be something as simple as getting more sleep! Anything that comes up that makes your heart sing when you tap into it. It works best if you focus most on the feeling of what it will be like when your dreams come true, than getting bogged down in specific details. I used to follow Mike Dooley, whose mantra was to focus on the "Wows not the Hows!" Let the universe take care of the details, you keep focussed on the bigger picture of your desire and how wonderful it will feel when you manifest it. Then take whatever small steps you can to put that dream into practice. Daily dreaming and daily action means success is inevitable. Of course, it won't happen overnight, but you will be given enough little signs and blessings from the universe, that you will feel that elation from knowing you are on the right path. The elation that is missing from life when we don't allow ourselves to dream. The elation that is the best high in the world, and turns us away from all the foods and drinks that dull our consciousness. When you live life in a state of elevation, you don't want to disrupt that with anything that's going to take you away from yourself, you want to keep expanding into it, and you want to increase your intake of substances that assist and support that expansion, like sunlight, superfoods and yoga.

Dreaming is the most important thing you can do. Make time for it every day.

Identifying Your Purpose

What is it that you really dream of? Everyone has a yearning for something else, no matter who you are or how good your apparent situation is. Desire for the next thing is healthy, and part of what makes us human. To desire is to have a dream, and that dream is your destiny. It's tapping into the greater picture, and seeing what the next step could be. The clearer the vision, the more we are driven to take action towards it. The action isn't always the fun part! The action, more often than not, can be challenging and tedious. But that strengthens our vision and our clarity around what we really want to achieve. If we have the determination to stick it out and make it happen, then the rewards are always immeasurably worth it.

Having a purpose is so key, and taking steps to meet it on a daily basis is essential for our soul growth. It doesn't matter how big or small those steps are, but to feel that we are constantly making progress makes us happy. Your purpose is unlikely to be what your parents or your teachers wanted for you. The more outlandish and far-fetched the dream, the more you know that you are on track. I am utterly convinced that courage and faith have as much currency as love and gratitude. There are some frequencies that the universe responds well to, and gratitude is probably the strongest. But courage is also near the top of the list: the more we strike out on a limb, the more the universe conspires to help us. The universe doesn't like it when we play it safe, so then things are more likely to become stuck and stagnant. Be bold, and take small steps towards your big dream every day, trusting that you will be supported. Your purpose will change and grow – don't be afraid to grow with it.

So many people don't have a clear purpose in life. They are going along with the crowd, not questioning where it's leading them. But sooner or later, a crisis will occur, and your lack of purpose will become an issue. It can take years to work out where you want to go with your life - better to do that when you are younger and you have everything ahead of you, than wait until you are older and have to turn the ship around (although it really is never too late). Your purpose doesn't need to be anything grand. Just a clear defined end, that it makes you feel happy to be working towards. Something that gives you a sense of completion and fulfilment when you think about it. ***Having this overarching narrative is essential to your happiness in life, both for men and women,*** *but as men are testosterone - eg, goal-driven - they find it easier to tap into their goals and focus on them. Women are much more likely to be derailed by the needs and demands of those around them, and put their own wishes at the bottom of the list.* An empowered woman switches those priorities around. It's a subtle but profound shift. You can still have the same balance of activities in your daily life – career, family, home, social life, partner – but to organise them so the ones that make you happy come first, rather than the ones that are expected of you, changes the whole scenario substantially. No longer will you find yourself always in situations where you are having to compromise or dissimulate, but instead you will find yourself respected, appreciated, and listened to. It may take a while for the people around you to adjust, but it's also healthy for them to become less dependent on you and build their own inner strength.

We all pick up in very unconscious ways, whether someone is motivated by pleasing themselves or pleasing others. You may think that pleasing others will make you more popular, but it's not the case! If you're a people pleaser, you will draw to you people who, often unconsciously, want to take advantage of that, and you will continually find yourself coming up against situations where people undermine you even though you felt you only had the best interests for them. When your primary motivation is to get what you need out of the day, people actually respond to your charisma, and are drawn to find out what makes you tick. You attract in people who want to help you manifest your dreams and your goals, because that's what you want for yourself. Rather this than attracting people who are always derailing you, because you are giving out clear signals that say you are allowing yourself to be derailed at any opportunity that might serve other people.

If you feel like your life isn't reflecting your true purpose, try to take some time out if at all possible to identify what that purpose is, and how you could begin to take steps towards it. As soon as you start on the right path for you, support and help will flow towards you. If you feel you are living a lifestyle that reflects your own manifest destiny, then it's still important to keep checking in with yourself, that you are doing truly what you want to do, and remind yourself how lucky you are. Keep creating new micro-goals for yourself so things don't become stagnant. Taking daily steps towards a purpose that you feel fully aligned with is a vital part of happiness.

Community

For women, our most powerful healing medicine is the most straight-forward. Talking from the heart, speaking our truth, has the ability to take so much pressure off. The problem nowadays is that not only do we not make enough time for deeper, more intimate encounters, when we do, we may be so far out of our comfort zone, we can't even connect with what we need to express. The vast majority of our conversation happens electronically – and while I use, love and appreciate Skype, Gmail, Instagram, Whatsapp, etc etc, these methods of communication don't give me the same biochemical satisfaction that a physical encounter does. You need an actual physical body in front of you before you start producing oxytocin and serotonin in the amounts you need to feel fulfilled.

Carving out time for your girlfriends is essential to your health. Anything where you can feel nurtured and supported by your sisters. I try to make room for a special lady at least a couple of times a week. Just an hour over juice or tea is enough to reset my biochemistry. If we can't meet in real life, Skype or a phone call is better than not at all.

If you can't find the community you need in your area, then build it! You can't be the only one feeling that something is lacking. It's one of my favourite parts of the courses that I teach, seeing the new friendships being built. People connect and stay friends after the course, often going on to work together on a venture such as a catering business or yoga retreats. Whatever you perceive as a lack in your life, is always an opportunity waiting to be filled! A wise friend started up a raw-food pot-luck group in her area, and she said, even if only one person came, it would be more fun than eating on her own. I think only one person did turn up to the first one, but it wasn't long before more than 20 people were showing up and they had to find a new venue.

178

"Talking to a friend who is calming and will just listen and then laugh with me always helps." **Claire**

Detox Techniques

I am a great believer in utilising traditional naturopathic techniques as a way of keeping our bodies in tip top condition. Like servicing a boiler, or getting your car MOT'd, these practices help keep everything running at peak performance. If we employ these techniques in our 20s and 30s, we are going to set ourselves up for a more healthy and productive middle age. If we use them when we are older, they can help restore our zest and energy for life. They are by no means necessary, but an invaluable support tool should you choose to engage with them just once or twice a year. Cleansing techniques are most effective when practiced around a New Moon, as the start of a new lunar cycle, and around the Equinox and Solstice times, as the start of a new solar cycle.

Please note, I am not a trained naturopath, and if you have any kind of chronic condition or are unsure of your health in anyway, I recommend consulting a professional before embarking on these programmes.

Liver Cleanse

The liver is where we hold anger; after a liver cleanse, expect to feel much lighter and less bothered about stuff that may have upset you in the past. If you are holding onto a lot of anger, perhaps regarding a relationship or a living situation, then you might find a liver flush a difficult thing to go through, as all those issues will raise up and ask you to deal with them head on.

As the main organ of detoxification, the liver carries a heavy burden. If you're trying to detoxify from an unhealthy diet, or particularly recreational drugs and alcohol, then I would say that a liver flush is an essential part of this process.

Liver flushes were popularised by two people - Andreas Moritz and Hulda Clark. Moritz has a great little book called The Liver and Gallbladder Miracle Cleanse, if you want to delve into it further. If you go online and research, there are a lot of different protocols, and you may get confused as to what is really going to work for you. What I share here is my experience of what works best, but it's by no means definitive.

If a full on liver flush is too much for you, you can make it more gentle by spreading it out over a month. Every morning, first thing, take 1 tablespoon of lemon juice combined with 1 tablespoon of olive oil, and wait at least 30 minutes before intaking anything else. Do this for 28 days and then take 28 days off. You can cycle like this, 28 days on, 28 days off, for as long as you need.

I also have a recipe which I call **The Lovely Little Liver Flush**. This is something you can do on a weekend, or any time you have a whole day to relax. Fast for the day (no solid foods, juices and teas are great), and then late afternoon, blend up the ingredients and drink down. The following day, book yourself a colonic or do an enema to receive the full benefits.

- 1 large or 2 small ruby grapefruit
- 2 lemons, juiced
- 2 tbsp flax oil
- 1 tsp probiotic powder
- 1 clove garlic
- 2cm root ginger
- ¼ tsp cayenne pepper
- 250ml water

Peel the grapefruit, and put them in your blender. Add all the rest of the ingredients apart from the water and blend to a soup. Once there are no bits left, add the water and blend again. This will work better in a high power blender – if you don't have one, press the garlic first and chop the ginger finely. Once it's blended, drink it down slowly. If it makes you feel nauseous, that's good!

The Complete Liver Flush needs a bit more time and effort, but it's definitely worth it if you feel you have anger management issues, or need to detoxify something out of your system. It's best to do the flush over a weekend when you have no other commitments, and spend a few days beforehand preparing for it, and a few days afterwards finishing it off properly. These preliminary and post-days can be fitted in around your normal schedule, as long as you are not crazy busy.

For three days prior, start to limit your intake of fats, so you are semi-fasting. Eat as cleanly as possible, and restrict yourself to fruit and vegetables as much as possible. You need to take some apple juice or apple cider vinegar, as the pectin in the apples will help soften the gallstones and make them more easy to release. Choose between one litre of fresh pressed (not pasteurised) apple juice, or 250ml (1 cup apple cider vinegar). This can be drunk throughout the day.

On the day of the flush, reduce your intake to liquids only, or eat as lightly as you can. You are going to do your flush in the late afternoon or early evening, and after that you won't want to go anywhere, so make sure you have everything you need ready for a cosy night in: a hot water bottle, books and movies, a pot of tea. When you're ready, I recommend blending up **500ml (2 cups) grapefruit juice with 250ml (1 cup) extra virgin olive oil**. Sip it down, and relax. You may feel sick, you may just drop off straight to sleep, these are completely normal reactions.

In the morning, you should wake feeling pretty awful, like you have a hangover, because that's effectively what you have, albeit self-induced. Your liver is working on overdrive to rid itself of what it doesn't want, although rather than it being last night's alcohol it is chucking out, it's months or even years of accumulated toxins that the grapefruit-olive oil mixture has triggered it into releasing. Be really gentle on yourself this day, take it easy, and just observe any emotions that come out without hanging onto them. A coffee enema is a really good idea, to stimulate the bile duct into releasing more stones. A colonic would also be a wonderful option.

For three days afterwards, it's super helpful if you can do castor oil packs. These will assist your body in releasing any residual toxins. A castor oil pack is the simplest of all the detox techniques. You just need castor oil, which you can pick up from any pharmacy, and packing fabric, for which an old tea towel or baby muslin will do. Castor oil is viscous and it stains, so wear old clothes while you do this; I have a t-shirt and jogging pants I have reserved for the purpose. Prepare a hot water bottle. Pour the oil onto the fabric and then press the fabric onto your liver (underneath your rib cage on the right). Put the hot water bottle on top, and lay still for at least an hour, to give the oil a chance to soak into the skin. A plastic bag over the fabric may help to stop the oil getting everywhere, or you can even cling wrap the fabric onto yourself! Do this for three evenings in the row, and you should perceive a remarkable difference in your mood and energy levels.

Kidney Cleanse

In Chinese medicine, the kidneys are where we store Jing energy. Jing is our reserve, our storehouse of energy, if you like. In our modern world, most of us are running on empty and depleting our Jing energy. This is why it's important to take good care of the kidneys! Not to mention the fact that, along with the liver, they do a lot of detoxification work for us.

The best way to do a Kidney Cleanse is to take one of the many herbal supplements on the market. I recommend brands such as Garden of Life or Nature's Answer. Any Chinese formulations to promote Jing energy will be helpful: I love Super Morning Jing from Shaman Shack, and Restore the Jing from Jing Herbs. Dragon Herbs also do excellent formulations.

Gut Cleanse

When cleansing the gut, the most important food groups to eliminate are dairy and gluten, these are the two that are the hardest to digest and cause the biggest build up of residue in the gut. Just simply cutting out on dairy and gluten can reduce a lot of the brain fog, mood swings, and bloating and flatulence that so many suffer with.

It's imperative that you include probiotic foods and drinks in your diet on a daily basis. Choose from the drinks such as kefir, kombucha, and jun; vegan foods such as seed cheese, sauerkraut and kimchi; unpasteurised macrobiotic products like miso and tempeh; and unpasteurised cheeses and yogurts (I enjoy coconut yoghurt, you could also include sheep's and goats' products, but I would steer away from cows' products as these are hard for the body to break down).

If you have a week digestive system, consider a probiotic supplement and a course of digestive enzymes. With probiotic supplements, the quality varies hugely, and it really is a question of you get what you pay for, so consider what you need it for, and what strength you believe will benefit you the most. Taking a good quality probiotic (the good ones are around £30 for a month's supply, in combination with a good quality digestive enzyme such as E3 enzymes, will strengthen your digestive system no end.

Lastly, I am an avid believer in colonics and enemas. I recommend an enema at least once a month, and colonics at least twice a year to maintain healthy gut function. Personally, I do twice as much as that! Two enemas a month and four colonics a year. It's a sad but true fact that our bodies, minds and immune systems are under such an onslaught these days, that we really need these cleansing techniques to help us avoid going under.

An enema is something you can do yourself at home, whereas a colonic is administered by a therapist in a centre. An enema only goes part way up the intestine, whereas a colonic does the full area so is a lot more effective. An enema session at home should take less than an hour: all you need is an enema bag and some undisturbed time. A colonic session also takes around an hour.

Bibliography

Venus on Fire, Mars on Ice - John Gray

The Female Brain – Louann Brizendine

The Male Brain – Louann Brizendine

Women's Bodies, Women's Wisdom – Dr Christine Northrup

The Wisdom of Menopause – Dr Christine Northrup

The Hormone Cure – Sara Gottfried

Calling in the One – Katherine Woodward Thomas

When Will I Ever Be Good Enough – Dr Karyl McBride

Misconceptions – Naomi Wolf

A Life's Work – Rachel Cusk

Sexual Politics – Kate Millett

The Change - Germaine Greer

How To Be a Woman - Caitlin Moran

Women Who Run with Wolves – Clarissa Pinkola Estes

My Life on the Road - Gloria Steinem

Marcelle Pick womentowomen.com website

Hormones: A Very Short Introduction by Martin Luck

Sweetening the Pill by Holly Grigg-Spall

All the Rebel Women: The Rise of the Fourth Wave of Feminism - Kira Cochrane

Resources

KateMagic.com for recipes, articles, interviews and events.
RawLiving.eu for all your raw vegan superfood needs.

To invite Kate to speak at your event, or to hold an Empowered Woman workshop in your area, email **kate@rawliving.eu**.

To join The Empowered Woman facebook group, find Kate Magic on facebook and then go to Groups, or use this link **https://tinyurl.com/ empoweredwoman2019**. The facebook group contains many links so you can further your own research, or ask questions.

Everything is a work in progress. If you spot any errors or inconsistencies, email **kate@rawliving.eu**. If you would like to be sent The Empowered Woman questionnaire, and have your responses included in a future edition of the book, please also email **kate@rawliving.eu**.

Previous books by Kate:
Eat Smart Eat Raw
Raw Living
Raw Magic
Raw Transitions

*"Kate Magic's Empowered Woman work is **a complete illumination into feminine power.** Her talks on how hormones play a crucial role in our lives are upbeat and insightful. A treasure of information, I will reflect on her teachings for years to come. I recommend this work to all women who want to Know Thyself!"*
Annie Jubb

"Attending Kate's course was the best thing I've ever done. So much information. It was the most life-affirming, inspirational, validating, clarifying life experience."
Kathryn Jansen